D0265761

Intermediate
Food Hygiene

A text for Intermediate Food Hygiene courses
and a reference for supervisors

Richard A. Sprenger,
BSc(Hons), DMS, FCIEH, MREHIS, FSOFHT

Managing Director Highfield.co.uk Limited

First published October 1999
Reprinted 2000, 2001, 2002, 2003, 2004, 2005
7th Edition 2005

PUBLISHED BY
©HIGHFIELD.CO.UK LIMITED

'Vue Pointe' Spinney Hill, Sprotbrough, Doncaster, DN5 7LY, UK
Tel: +44 0845 2260350   Facsimile: +44 0845 2260360
E-mail: richard@highfield.co.uk

Websites: www.highfield.co.uk www.foodsafetytrainers.co.uk

ISBN 1-904544-45-2

Printed by Trafford Press • Telephone: 01302 367509

Contents

Preface

The prevention of most food poisoning outbreaks is relatively simple and well understood. Cook food thoroughly, protect it from contamination and keep it cold or hot.

But despite our knowledge of these simple controls and the millions of first-tier food handlers, who have attended food hygiene courses, the number of cases of food poisoning remains at an unacceptable level. Attendance on food hygiene courses alone, even when obtaining certificates, appears to have had little effect. It could be argued that on-the-job training to promote competency, and effective instruction, supervision and control are an even more important part of the overall strategy necessary to significantly reduce levels of foodborne illness and food complaints. In other words knowledgeable and competent supervisors and managers are the key to food safety.

I have written this book with the intention of providing supervisors and middle managers with the essential, practical information to enable them to manage staff to provide safe food. 'Intermediate Food Hygiene' is based on the syllabuses of the Intermediate Food Safety Courses provided by the Chartered Institute of Environmental Health, the Royal Environmental Health Institute of Scotland, the Royal Institute of Public Health and the Royal Society for the Promotion of Health.

In addition to assisting candidates to successfully complete the above courses, 'Intermediate Food Hygiene' should be used as a reference to help supervisors make correct decisions with regard to food safety. Emphasis has been placed on the measures necessary to control the most common reasons for food poisoning outbreaks, including temperature control, effective cooling, storage and thawing, preventing contamination and the destruction of food poisoning bacteria.

Many of the food scares relating to, for example, salmonella in eggs, E. coli O157, listeria and high levels of food poisoning would probably not have occurred if the highest standards of hygiene had been observed and the recommendations in this book had been followed.

If you rigorously apply the principles of food safety detailed throughout 'Intermediate Food Hygiene', you should avoid your food business becoming one of the food poisoning statistics or, even worse, starting off the next food scare.

1 An introduction to food safety

Safe food is food which is free of contaminants and will not cause illness or harm. Persons involved in food poisoning investigations often remark about the cleanliness of the premises responsible. If food hygiene is intended to ensure the safety of food and prevent food poisoning then it follows that hygiene is more than cleanliness; it involves all measures necessary to ensure the safety and wholesomeness of food during preparation, processing, manufacture, storage, transportation, distribution, handling, sale and supply. This involves:

♦ protecting food from risk of contamination, i.e. preventing objectionable matter getting into food, including harmful bacteria, poisons and foreign bodies;

♦ preventing any bacteria present multiplying to a level which would result in illness of consumers or the early spoilage of food;

♦ destroying any harmful bacteria in the food by thorough cooking, processing or irradiation; and

♦ discarding unfit or contaminated food.

The cost of poor hygiene and food poisoning

Persons carrying on a food business have legal, commercial and moral obligations to provide safe food. The costs resulting from food poisoning can be very high, as are those from poor hygiene. These costs, both financial and social, fall on employers and employees as well as those persons who are ill. Costs for employers include:

♦ the loss of working days, and productivity, from illness caused by employee seating contaminated food;

Bad hygiene - lower profits!

♦ the closure of food premises, or the prohibition of processes by local authority action;

♦ brand damage. A loss of business and reputation, either from bad publicity or from public reaction to poor standards, food poisoning outbreaks and even deaths;

♦ increased risk of pest infestation;

♦ fines and costs of legal action taken because of contraventions of hygiene legislation or because of the sale of unfit or unsatisfactory food;

♦ civil action taken by food poisoning sufferers, or those aggrieved by injury or trauma from foreign bodies in food;

♦ food losses due to premature spoilage or damage, because of poor stock rotation, incorrect storage temperature or pest infestations;

♦ low staff morale, higher turnover with attendant costs and inefficiencies from staff unwilling or unable to tolerate poor standards;

♦ food complaints and costs of internal investigation and decontamination; and

♦ loss of production.

Food employees may suffer by:
- losing their jobs because of closure, loss of business or because they become long-term carriers of food poisoning organisms, especially salmonella; and
- losing overtime or bonuses.

The benefits of high standards of hygiene

Good hygiene - higher profits!

- Satisfied customers, a good reputation which creates greater confidence and increased business.
- Brand protection.
- Compliance with food safety legislation.
- Less food wastage and increased shelf-life. ·
- Good working conditions, higher staff morale and lower staff turnover, which promotes increased productivity.
- Reduced risk of food poisoning and food complaints.

High-risk foods

High-risk foods are ready-to-eat foods which, under favourable conditions, support the multiplication of pathogenic bacteria and are intended for consumption without treatment which would destroy such organisms. High-risk foods are most likely to be involved in cases of food poisoning. They are usually high in protein, requiring strict temperature control and protection from contamination and include:
- all cooked meat and poultry;
- cooked meat products including liquid gravy, stock, pâté and meat pies;
- milk, cream, artificial cream, custards and dairy produce;
- cooked eggs/products, especially those products made with raw eggs and not thoroughly cooked, for example, mousse, mayonnaise and home-made ice cream;
- shellfish and other seafoods, for example, cooked prawns and oysters; and
- cooked rice (not high in protein).

Low-risk foods

These foods are rarely implicated in food poisoning and may be stored, suitably packaged, at ambient temperatures. They do not support the multiplication of food poisoning bacteria. Examples include:
- preserved food such as jam;
- dried foods or food with little available moisture, such as flour, bread, biscuits. On adding liquid to powdered food, such as milk, the food becomes high-risk;
- acid foods, such as vinegar or products stored in vinegar;
- fermented products, such as salami;
- foods with high fat/sugar content, such as chocolate (chocolate is occasionally

responsible for salmonella outbreaks); and

♦ canned foods, whilst unopened.

Ready-to-eat raw foods

Unfortunately an increasing number of outbreaks of foodborne illness are attributed to the consumption of raw, ready-to-eat foods which are stored at ambient temperatures, for example, salad vegetables, melons, raspberries and unpasteurized apple juice. As these foods don't usually support the multiplication of pathogens, the organisms involved are capable of causing illness in very low numbers, for example, viruses, *E. coli* O157, shigella and parasites.

Salmonella outbreaks have been associated with cut melon, lettuce and apple juice. Lettuce, raspberries and apple juice have been the food vehicle for outbreaks of viral illness and *E. coli* O157. Sewage contamination or bad hygiene practices during harvesting are the most likely causes of outbreaks. Ready-to-eat raw foods should be washed and preferably disinfected before use.

Raw foods (intended for cooking/processing)

Raw foods are often contaminated with large numbers of food poisoning bacteria, for example, raw meat, poultry, eggs and root vegetables contaminated with soil. If raw foods are perishable, they should be stored in a refrigerator separate from high-risk and ready-to-eat food. Raw food may present a serious risk of food poisoning if not cooked thoroughly, especially poultry, products made with raw egg, bivalves, such as oysters, and raw milk.

Food poisoning

Food poisoning is usually an acute illness resulting from eating contaminated or poisonous food. It excludes allergies to food or toxins. The symptoms normally include one or more of the following: abdominal pain, diarrhoea, vomiting and nausea.

Gastroenteritis

This term is used to refer to an inflammation of the stomach and intestinal tract that normally results in diarrhoea.

Carriers

Carriers are people who show no symptoms of illness but excrete food poisoning or foodborne pathogens which may contaminate food, for example, salmonellae or shigellae. Organisms may be excreted intermittently.

Convalescent carriers are people who have recovered from an illness but still harbour the organism. The convalescent state may be quite prolonged and salmonellae are sometimes excreted for several months.

Healthy carriers are people who have displayed no symptoms but harbour the causative organism. Healthy carriers may have become infected with pathogenic bacteria from contact with raw food with which they work, particularly poultry or meat.

Allergy

An identifiable immunological response to food or food additives may be described as an allergy. The allergen is usually a protein and several systems within the body may be affected, for example, the respiratory system, the gastrointestinal tract, the skin and the central nervous system. Symptoms vary considerably and may include bronchitis, vomiting, diarrhoea, a rash and migraine. Reactions may be mild or extremely severe and may occur immediately the food is consumed, or up to 48 hours later. An allergic response should not be confused with food poisoning. The first exposure to the specific food, for example, peanuts or sesame seeds, does not produce symptoms; however, subsequent exposure results in a typical allergic response, or even death. Around one in two hundred people may have a peanut allergy.

THE INCIDENCE OF FOOD POISONING IN ENGLAND & WALES

The annual incidence of food poisoning is unknown. Several million people in England and Wales suffer from gastroenteritis each year; many of these will have food poisoning and a few will die. Those most at risk include the young, the elderly, the immunocompromised and pregnant women.

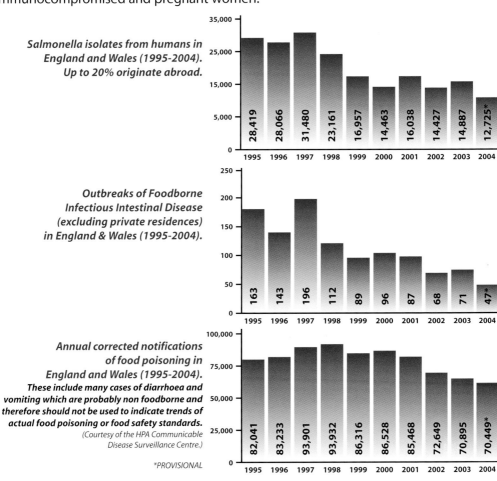

Salmonella isolates from humans in England and Wales (1995-2004). Up to 20% originate abroad.

Outbreaks of Foodborne Infectious Intestinal Disease (excluding private residences) in England & Wales (1995-2004).

Annual corrected notifications of food poisoning in England and Wales (1995-2004).
These include many cases of diarrhoea and vomiting which are probably non foodborne and therefore should not be used to indicate trends of actual food poisoning or food safety standards.
(Courtesy of the HPA Communicable Disease Surveillance Centre.)

*PROVISIONAL

2 Microbiology

Microbiology is the study of microscopic plants and animals and this includes bacteria, moulds and yeasts. The most important microorganisms of interest to the food industry are bacteria, and bacteriology is the study of bacteria. If food handlers are to understand food safety and how to prevent food poisoning, they must have some understanding of basic bacteriology.

Bacteria are single-celled microorganisms which are found everywhere: on raw food and people, in soil, air and water. A microorganism is an organism that is so small it can only be seen under a powerful microscope. Most bacteria are harmless and some are essential, for example, for breaking down decaying matter. Others are of benefit to the food industry, for example, in the manufacture of cheese and yoghurt. Unfortunately a small number of bacteria cause food spoilage and others, known as pathogens, cause illness including food poisoning.

Commensals are bacteria which live on or in the body without causing illness. Most bacteria on the body are commensals and are part of the normal flora. For example, some species of staphylococcus are found on the skin and in the mouth or nose. Other species are transient and may cause skin infections, such as boils. If harmful species of staphylococcus are transferred to high-risk food, they may cause illness.

The size, shape and structure of bacteria

Bacteria can only be observed under a microscope with a magnification of around 1000 times. Bacteria vary in size from around .001mm to .003mm. Although an individual bacterium cannot be seen, large numbers can be seen as small white or yellow spots on growth media in laboratories. These spots are known as colonies. Large numbers of spoilage organisms may also cause visible effects on food, for example, discolouration, slime and odour.

Bacteria vary considerably in shape:

- ◆ Cocci are spherical;   ◆   Rods are sausage-shaped;
- ◆ Spirochaetes are spiral; and   ◆   Vibrios are comma-shaped;

| Cocci | Rods | Spirochaetes | Vibrios |

Cell wall – a rigid structure that gives the bacterium its shape.
Cell membrane – controls passage of waste and nutrients into and out of the cell.
Cytoplasm – the 'body' of the bacterium.
Nuclear material – the 'brain' of the bacterium (gives genetic characteristics).
Flagella – attachments that allow bacteria to move in liquids.

Although some bacteria can use flagella to swim around in liquids, most bacteria rely on other objects to move them about, for example, moving from one food to another using a table top, a piece of equipment such as a knife or the hands of the food handler. Things which transfer bacteria from one place to another are known as vehicles.

As food poisoning bacteria are commonly found on raw food and people, it is impracticable to operate a food business without food poisoning bacteria being present at one time or another. It is therefore essential to deny them the conditions which would allow them to multiply to a level where they present a risk to customers. (Large numbers of bacteria usually need to be present in food to cause food poisoning.)

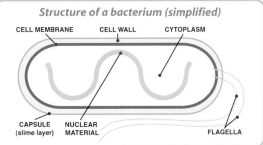

Structure of a bacterium (simplified)

CELL MEMBRANE   CELL WALL   CYTOPLASM

CAPSULE   NUCLEAR
(slime layer)   MATERIAL   FLAGELLA

Bacterial multiplication

Bacteria reproduce by splitting into two. This process is known as binary fission and the time taken between each division (generation time) varies considerably depending on, among other things, temperature and the nutrients (food) available. In optimum (ideal) conditions some food poisoning bacteria can split in two every ten minutes, although at temperatures of around 10°C it may take up to ten hours or they may stop multiplying. The average generation time of the common food poisoning bacteria under optimum conditions is usually considered to be around 20 minutes. When bacteria are growing and multiplying this is described as the vegetative state.

If food is contaminated a common level of contamination may be around 1000 bacteria per gram of food. If this food provides optimum conditions then within one hour 40 minutes, these bacteria could double every ten minutes and become 1,000,000. This number of bacteria is likely to cause food poisoning. The multiplication of pathogens in food is a hazard.

Nutrients

Food poisoning bacteria obtain their essential basic nutrients from amino acids, fats, vitamins and minerals, which are usually provided by high protein food such as meat, fish and dairy produce. Foods with high sugar and salt content are usually unsuitable and therefore are unlikely to support bacterial multiplication.

Moisture

Bacteria require water to transport nutrients into the cell and take away waste products. With the exception of dehydrated products such as milk powder, most foods contain sufficient moisture to enable bacteria to multiply. However, some bacteria can survive dehydration and when liquid is added to the dried food it once again becomes a high-risk food and must be stored under refrigeration.

Acidity and alkalinity (pH)

The pH of a food is measured on a scale of 1 to 14. Acid foods have pH values below 7, alkaline foods above 7 and a pH value of 7 is neutral. Most bacteria will not multiply in a pH below 4.5, i.e. an acid food such as fruit juice. However, if a large number of food poisoning bacteria are introduced into an acid food it may take some time for the bacteria to die. For this reason we must protect acid food from contamination at all times.

Temperature

Bacteria have a maximum and minimum temperature for multiplication as well as an optimum temperature when multiplication is the most rapid. Most food poisoning bacteria grow best at around 37°C

Bacterial growth curve which shows the four stages of bacterial growth when, for example, food is removed from a refrigerator.

(body temperature) although *Clostridium perfringens* prefers 46°C. The common food poisoning bacteria will not multiply below 5°C or above 52°C. However, many can survive outside this temperature range and start multiplying again when temperatures are suitable. The range of temperature, which is likely to encourage the fastest multiplication, is between 20°C and 50°C. Some pathogens will grow between 0°C and 20°C but they multiply more slowly at the lower temperatures.

Some food spoilage bacteria multiply slowly under refrigeration, which is one of the reasons for food becoming unfit if stored longer than the recommended shelf-life.

Psychrophiles are bacteria which prefer temperatures below 20°C. Mesophiles prefer temperatures of 20°C to 50°C and this group includes the common food poisoning bacteria. Thermophiles multiply most rapidly above 45°C.

Presence of oxygen

Some bacteria can only multiply in the presence of oxygen and others can only multiply when there is no oxygen. The former bacteria are known as aerobes and the latter anaerobes. Many bacteria can multiply with or without the presence of oxygen and these are called facultative anaerobes, for example, salmonella.

Oxygen is normally present in food except in the case of liquids which have been thoroughly boiled. Cooking, for example, joints of meat, also drives off oxygen and the centre then provides ideal conditions for anaerobes.

Toxin production

Food poisoning bacteria produce toxins (poisons) which cannot be detected by visual inspection. Toxins may be either exotoxins or endotoxins.

Exotoxins are produced during multiplication or sporulation of bacteria. Quite often exotoxins are released into the food and many are heat resistant, so that even if cooking destroys the bacteria, the toxin may remain and cause illness if the food is eaten. This results in a short onset time. Enterotoxins are exotoxins that affect the gastrointestinal tract.

Endotoxins form part of the bacterial cell wall and are released on the death of the bacteria, usually in the intestines of persons consuming contaminated food. If the toxin is produced in the intestine, the onset period, for the first symptoms to appear, will usually be longer than if the toxin is in the food.

Spore formation

Some food poisoning bacteria, such as *Clostridium perfringens*, *Bacillus cereus* and *Clostridium botulinum* are able to form spores which are capable of surviving unfavourable conditions such as high temperatures, dehydration and the use of disinfectants. Spores are round protective bodies which form inside the bacterial cell and may allow survival for many years without food and water. They cannot be detected by visual inspection. When favourable conditions return, the spores split open and release the vegetative bacteria which then grow and multiply.

Temperatures in excess of 100°C are often required for long periods (as much as five hours) to destroy spores. The temperature used to ensure the safety of low-acid canned food, by destroying spores of *Clostridium botulinum*, is the equivalent of 121°C for three minutes.

Competition

When there are many different bacteria present, they will compete for the same food. Fortunately, most food poisoning bacteria are not as competitive as the normal flora found on food and, unless present in high numbers, will usually die.

Destruction of bacteria

Food poisoning bacteria can be destroyed by using high temperatures for sufficient time. The higher the temperature, the shorter the time required. However, the type of bacteria (whether or not they produce spores), the number of bacteria present and the type of food also affect the time needed to kill bacteria and make the food safe. Bacteria will start to die at around 55°C. However, a core temperature of greater than 75°C is required when cooking food to be reasonably confident that

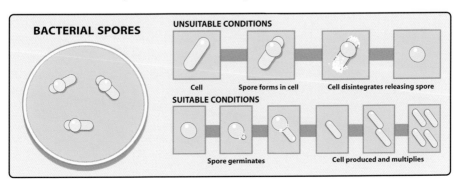

BACTERIAL SPORES

UNSUITABLE CONDITIONS

Cell   Spore forms in cell   Cell disintegrates releasing spore

SUITABLE CONDITIONS

Spore germinates   Cell produced and multiplies

most harmful bacteria will have been destroyed.

Unfortunately, much higher temperatures are required to destroy toxins and spores produced by some food poisoning bacteria. Spores are much more resistant to drying, boiling, disinfectants and other conditions, which usually destroy vegetative food poisoning bacteria. The survival of bacteria, spores or toxins is a hazard.

Bacteria can also be destroyed by irradiation chemicals, such as nitrates, salt or sugar, u/v light, steam or the use of disinfectants such as bleach. Freezing cannot be used to destroy bacteria as most will survive the freezing process and long periods of storage at freezing temperatures.

Moulds

Moulds are aerobic chlorophyll-free fungi which produce thread-like filaments (hyphae) and form a branched network of mycelium. Moulds, which may be black, white or of various colours, will grow on most foods, whether moist or dry, acid or alkaline and high in salt or sugar concentrations. The optimum growth temperature is usually 20°C to 30°C, although they will grow well over a wide range of temperatures and may cause problems in refrigerators. Growth has been recorded as low as 10°C. High humidities and fluctuating temperatures accelerate mould growth.

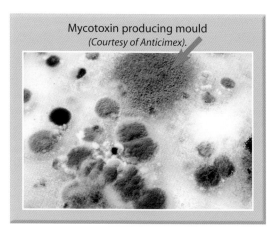

Mycotoxin producing mould
(Courtesy of Anticimex).

Moulds commonly affect bread and other bakery products, and although spores are usually destroyed in baking, subsequent contamination is difficult to avoid. Mould inhibitors are usually added to bread.

Food must always be stored in accordance with the manufacturer's instructions and never sold outside its 'use-by' date. Mishandling of vacuum packs of cheese may result in punctures and consequential mould growth. As the mycelium grows over the food, hyphae penetrate the substance and consequently mould soon returns if scraped off the surface. Regular checking of stock is imperative to avoid customer complaints. The presence of mould on food is usually considered to render it unfit for human consumption. Cheeses produced with specific moulds are an exception.

Yeasts

Yeasts are microscopic fungi which reproduce by budding. Most yeasts grow best in the presence of oxygen, although fermentative types may grow slowly anaerobically. The majority of yeasts prefer acid foods (pH 4 to 4.5) with a reasonable level of available moisture. However, many yeasts will grow in high concentrations of sugar and salt. The optimum growth temperature for yeast is around 25°C to 30°C with a maximum of around 47°C. Some yeasts can grow slowly at 0°C and below.

Yeasts are used in the manufacture of foods such as bread, beer and vinegar. However, they cause spoilage of many foods including jam, fruit juice, honey, meats and wines.

Viruses

Viruses are even smaller than bacteria and can only be seen under a very powerful electron microscope. They multiply in living cells, not in food. Some viruses cause illness, including viral gastroenteritis and hepatitis A.

Protozoa

Protozoa are single-celled organisms which form the basis of the food chain. They live in most habitats such as oceans, soil and decaying matter. Some are pathogenic and usually result in waterborne outbreaks. They do not multiply in food but their cysts may remain infectious in foods for a long time. Furthermore, they have a low infective dose, i.e. only small numbers of cysts are required to cause illness. Two pathogenic protozoa causing illness in the UK are *Cryptosporidium parvum* and *Giardia lamblia*.

Key points

♦   Bacteria are found everywhere but can only be seen under a microscope.
♦   Food businesses cannot operate without food poisoning bacteria being present at one time or another.
♦   Bacteria rely on food, people and equipment to move about in food premises.
♦   Bacteria require food, moisture, warmth and time to multiply.
♦   The common food poisoning bacteria prefer a temperature range of 20°C to 50°C for rapid multiplication.
♦   In optimum conditions, some food poisoning bacteria can multiply every ten minutes. The multiplication of pathogens within food is a hazard.
♦   Temperatures above 75°C are used to destroy bacteria but some exotoxins and spores may survive boiling for a considerable period. Survival of bacteria, spores or toxins is a hazard.
♦   Spores or toxins in food cannot be detected by visual inspection.
♦   Most food poisoning bacteria will not multiply in refrigerators below 5°C, but they will survive freezing.
♦   Food poisoning bacteria do not multiply in high acid food, high salt or sugar concentrations or dried foods (until reconstituted).

3 Food contamination and its prevention

Contamination of food is a major hazard and may be considered as the occurrence of any objectionable matter in or on the food. Therefore, carcasses may be contaminated with faecal material, high-risk food may be contaminated with spoilage or food poisoning bacteria and flour may be contaminated with rodent hairs. To prevent the consumption of food which is unacceptable or unsafe, contamination must be kept to a minimum.

There are three types of contamination:

♦ *Microbiological contamination by bacteria, moulds, viruses (microorganisms) or parasites.* Usually occurs in food premises because of ignorance, inadequate space, poor design or because of food handlers taking short cuts. In the early stages it will not be detectable. Contamination of this sort is the most serious and may result in food spoilage, food poisoning or even death.

♦ *Physical contamination by foreign bodies including insects.* Physical contamination may render food unfit or unsafe but often involves pieces of paper, plastic, metal or string and is usually unpleasant or a nuisance.

♦ *Chemical contamination.* Examples include pesticides on fruit and residues from cleaning chemicals.

CONTAMINATION BY MICROORGANISMS

Bacterial contamination is the most significant as it results in large amounts of spoilt food and unacceptable numbers of food poisoning cases. Food poisoning bacteria may be brought into food premises by the following sources:

♦ food handlers/visitors;

♦ raw foods including poultry, meat, eggs, milk, fish and shellfish and water especially when polluted with sewage or animal faeces. Vegetables or fruit may become contaminated from manure or polluted irrigation water;

♦ insects, rodents, animals and birds; and

♦ from the environment, including soil and dust.

Mould spores will be present in the atmosphere, on surfaces, especially damp surfaces, and on mouldy food. Food should always be covered and mouldy food must be segregated. Furthermore, mould must not be allowed to grow on walls, ceilings and window frames. Mould growth often occurs if food is stored at the wrong temperature, at high humidity and in excess of the recommended shelf-life. It may also affect cheese stored in vacuum packs which are pierced. Canned foods which are removed from cases opened with unguarded craft knives may become punctured, thus giving rise to mould growth inside the can.

Viruses are usually brought into food premises by food handlers who are carriers, or on raw food such as shellfish which have been grown in sewage-polluted water.

Vehicles and routes of bacterial contamination

Sometimes bacteria pass directly from the source to high-risk food, but as bacteria are largely static and as the sources are not always in direct contact with food, the bacteria have to rely on other things to transfer them to food. These things are known as vehicles and the main ones are:

- hands;
- hand-contact surfaces; and
- cloths and equipment;
- food-contact surfaces.

Cross-contamination can be defined as 'the transfer of bacteria from contaminated foods (usually raw) to other foods'. This includes direct contact, drip and indirect contamination by, for example, hands, equipment or work surfaces. The path along which bacteria are transferred from the source to the food is known as the route. Knowledge of sources, vehicles and routes is vital to food poisoning prevention, as different controls apply to each. It must be assumed that all sources are contaminated, i.e. every worker is a carrier and all raw meat, milk, animals, insects, used equipment and the surrounding environment are contaminated.

SOURCES, VEHICLES AND ROUTES OF CONTAMINATION

Prevention of contamination depends on either removing the sources, or putting barriers between them and the vehicles or between them and food. Thus human access to food must be restricted, raw foods handled in separate areas, vermin excluded and work areas enclosed in suitably constructed and ventilated rooms.

SOURCES ➞ VEHICLES ➞ HIGH-RISK FOODS

Similarly, vehicles must, where possible, be excluded. Handling should be minimized, wiping cloths used sparingly or destroyed after each use, hand-contact surfaces, such as tap handles, replaced with knee or electronically operated taps, and the number of surfaces with which the food comes into contact limited.

In the nature of food preparation, however, routes between sources and vehicles survive, giving rise to contaminated vehicles. Consequently, routes must be disrupted by cleaning and disinfection. For example, should a work surface come into contact with a contaminated source, raw meat for instance, the surface must be cleaned and disinfected before it is used for cooked meat.

CHECK LIST FOR CONTAMINATION CONTROL

♦ Purchase food and raw materials from known, reliable and hygienic suppliers. Test for quality and inspect suppliers' premises if appropriate.

♦ Accept deliveries only if transported in clean, properly equipped vehicles, with clean drivers wearing satisfactory protective clothing. Refrigerated vehicles may be necessary.

♦ Inspect deliveries immediately on arrival. Reject or segregate any damaged, unfit or contaminated material. Where relevant, check temperature, codes and date markings and reject out-of-date food.

♦ After checking, remove deliveries immediately to appropriate storage, refrigerator or cold store.

Unsatisfactory deliveries must be rejected

♦ Keep any unfit food, chemicals and refuse away from stored food. Use only food containers for storing food.

♦ Keep high-risk foods apart from raw foods at all times, in separate areas with separate utensils and equipment. Colour coding is useful. Separate food handlers are recommended.

♦ Maintain scrupulous personal hygiene at all times and handle food as little as possible. Exclude potential carriers.

♦ Keep food covered or otherwise protected unless it is actually being processed or prepared, in which case bring food out only when needed. Do not leave food lying around.

♦ Keep premises, equipment and utensils clean and in good condition and repair. Report or remedy defects with the minimum of delay. Disinfect food-contact surfaces, hand-contact surfaces and cleaning equipment.

♦ Ensure that all empty containers are clean and disinfected prior to filling with food.

♦ Control cleaning materials, particularly wiping cloths. Keep cleaning materials away from food. Remove food and food containers before cleaning. Care must be taken to ensure that all cleaning residues, including water, are drained from food equipment and pipes. Always clean from high-risk areas to low-risk areas.

♦ Remove waste food and refuse from food areas as soon as practicable. Store in appropriate containers, away from food.

♦ Maintain an active pest control programme.

♦ Control visitors and maintenance workers in high-risk areas. Ensure hygiene disciplines apply to all personnel, including management.

♦ Inspect food areas and processes frequently, act on any defects or unhygienic practices. Train staff and monitor performance. Food handlers and engineers must be aware of the bacteriological and physical contamination they may introduce.

♦ Ensure adequate thawing of foods, separate from other foods.

♦ Make suitable provisions for cooling food prior to refrigeration.

PHYSICAL CONTAMINATION (HAZARDS)

Foreign bodies found in food may be brought into food premises with the raw materials or introduced during storage, preparation, service or display. It is essential that supervisors are aware of the types of foreign bodies commonly found in their particular sector of the food industry and that they take all reasonable precautions and exercise all due diligence to secure their removal or prevent their introduction. Product traceability systems must be introduced. A record should be kept of all customer complaints and steps should be taken to identify the source of the contaminant.

Contamination of food by extraneous matter will cause customer dissatisfaction and may result in bad publicity. If press and media coverage results, the impact on the business can be disastrous leading, in the worst possible case, to loss of product confidence and even company viability. It is therefore in the interests of the manufacturer to minimize the risk of foreign body contamination.

Intrinsic foreign bodies, such as bones in chicken meat or stalks in vegetables, should be minimized by care in harvesting and processing, although foreign body detection and removal systems, such as the use of inspection belts, will also be necessary. The presence of foreign bodies in food, such as glass or rodent droppings, is usually of greater concern as this indicates a breakdown in hygiene and will not be tolerated by the consumer.

Common foreign bodies found in food

Although in the minority, some foreign bodies may be considered as a serious health hazard, such as glass, stones, wire or rodent droppings, which may result in cut mouths, dental damage, choking or illness.

However, all foreign bodies are, at the very least, a nuisance and manufacturers in particular must implement appropriate systems to prevent or remove such contamination. Their presence in food is likely to be an offence under food safety legislation. The hazard analysis and critical control point system (HACCP) provides the most effective preventive approach, especially for manufacturers, and will be extremely useful if the company wishes to avail itself of the due diligence defence in the event of a prosecution.

IDENTIFYING PHYSICAL HAZARDS AND CONTROL MEASURES
Raw materials

The variable nature of raw material quality may be a significant problem in food processing. Raw materials can be a major source of extraneous matter and food manufacturers use a range of cleaning, sorting and grading operations to separate out the offending material. In the manufacture of frozen peas for example, stones, metal screws, cigarette ends, stalks, sticks, caterpillars and dirt often accompany the vined peas as they arrive at the factory.

Control measures should include specifications to detail maximum permissible levels of contaminants in the incoming raw materials. By agreeing specifications with all suppliers and monitoring and evaluating the supplier performance in meeting the specifications, the company has an effective tool in minimizing the risk posed by extraneous matter.

Before using raw materials, cleaning or washing and inspection may need to be carried out. Most physical contamination has to be removed by food handlers as the vegetables pass along an illuminated inspection belt.

Liquids used in food production should be filtered and powders sieved. Filters, screens and sieves should be as fine as possible and must be cleaned and checked regularly. Worn equipment must be replaced. Wooden-framed sieves are usually unacceptable.

Packaging materials

Packaging may be a source of extraneous matter in the form of warehouse and transport dirt/dust, wood from the pallets, paper and polythene strips from over-wraps and a variety of insects and even rodents. Containers (cans, jars, bottles and plastic pots) may be used directly for filling with minimal cleaning and any rogue material in the container (metal splinters, glass, dirt, insects, etc.) may end up in the final product.

Staples, cardboard, string, fibres, cloth, rubber, plastic and polythene

Food may be delivered in various containers including paper sacks, cardboard boxes and polythene bags. Particular care is necessary when emptying containers to avoid contamination of food. As far as practicable, all unpacking and packing should be carried out in areas separate from food production or preparation, if open food is exposed to risk of contamination.

String removed from hessian sacks and ties removed from bags should immediately be placed in suitable containers provided specifically for the purpose. As an extra precaution, coloured string may be specified to aid detection should it end up in the product. Paper sacks should be cut open, although care must be exercised to ensure pieces of paper do not finish up in the food. It is preferable for raw materials to be emptied into suitable lidded containers and not dispensed direct from paper sacks.

Particular care is needed to ensure that staples, which tend to fly considerable distances when boxes are prised open, do not contaminate food. Suppliers should be requested to use adhesive tape to fasten boxes, instead of staples. Many products are delivered in black polythene bags and small pieces of polythene often end up in the product.

Effective measures in terms of good manufacturing practice should be adopted within the HACCP scheme to minimize the risk of contamination. An example would be the use of secondary packaging which is removed prior to primary packaging material entering a high-risk area.

The building, installations and equipment
Wood splinters

As far as possible the use of wood, especially soft wood, should be eliminated from food production areas. Wooden containers used for transporting raw materials should be phased out. Pallets should not be double stacked over open food.

Bolts, nuts and other pieces of metal

As far as practicable nuts should be self-locking. Bolts, nuts and screws should be non-corroding and positioned to ensure that, should they fall off equipment, they do not drop into the food.

Hazards from wood splinters, rust and flaking paint

Flaking paint or rust

Ceiling structure, pipes or equipment should be non-flaking and rust-free. This is especially important when such fixtures are positioned directly above open products. In some older factories this problem is very difficult to overcome and consequently additional protection is necessary, for example, enclosed systems for conveying food and empty containers such as cans. New factories should be designed so that fixtures, ducts and pipes are not suspended over working areas or food if the product is exposed to risk of contamination, for example, from condensation.

Grease and oil

Wherever necessary, food-grade grease and lubricants should be used. It is important that engineers use the minimum amount necessary to lubricate moving parts and that grease is not left on the machine. Careful control will ensure the absence of complaints relating to grease in food. It is preferable for motors not to be positioned above open food. When this occurs, suitable non-corroding, cleansable drip-trays should be fixed underneath to catch oil spillages.

Glass

The use of ordinary glass, porcelain and enamelware in food factories should be avoided. Perspex or wired glass windows should be used. Diffusers, or protective sleeves should be fitted to all fluorescent tubes in food rooms. All beakers, funnels, etc. used by the quality control staff in production areas should be unbreakable. Glass containers, other than those used for the final product, drinking cups, glass mirrors and gauges must all be eliminated from food production areas. Scales coated in vitreous enamel should be replaced, preferably by stainless steel. Particular care is necessary with glass containers used for product as any line breakages may result in glass contaminating other products.

Hazards from broken glass dials and windows

Notices

Notices used for warnings, advice or instructions should be properly fixed and permanent. Sheets of paper sellotaped to equipment or close to open food are unacceptable. Recipe instructions should be enclosed in sealed polythene bags. Notice boards should be kept out of areas where open food is handled and should be covered in perspex or similar sheeting.

Food handlers

Contaminants, which originate from personnel, include earrings, hair, fingernails, buttons, combs and pen tops. Protective clothing, including head covering, must be of a suitable type and worn correctly. The personal hygiene of food handlers must be beyond reproach, and earrings and jewellery, other than wedding rings, should not be worn. Pencils, pens and pieces of chalk must not be used in situations which expose food to risk of contamination, for example, near filling hoppers and mixing vessels.

Sweet papers, cigarette ends and matches are common contaminants and staff should not eat

Hazards from wood splinters, drawing pins, nails and pieces of paper

sweets, chew gum or smoke in food rooms. Regular training and reinforcement, such as posters, should be used together with strict supervision and enforcement of company rules.

Cleaning activities

Care must be taken during cleaning and all staff involved should be trained to ensure they do not expose product to risk of contamination by using worn equipment, especially brushes which are likely to lose their bristles, or by using inappropriate methods such as high pressure spraying during the production of open food. Particular care must be exercised when using paper towels or cloths to ensure small pieces of paper or cloth do not end up in the product.

Maintenance operatives

Engineers must be trained to take extra care when working with food equipment to ensure that they do not leave loose nuts, swarf and pieces of wire in food rooms on completion of maintenance. Temporary repairs with string should be avoided. It is good practice for managers to check areas where engineers or contractors have been working before food handling commences.

During production, areas which are being decorated or where repair or maintenance work is being carried out must be suitably segregated by screens, such as heavy-duty polythene, to avoid exposing product to risk of contamination. Maintenance workers should not wear grossly soiled overalls and should not stand on or climb over machinery or open food if there is the slightest risk of introducing contamination. If necessary, all food should be removed or protected with clean polythene sheeting. The use of ladders over open food or hoppers can result in dirt falling off shoes or rungs and ending up in the final product. After the work has been completed all tools, screws, swarf, grease, etc. must be removed and the area cleaned and, if necessary, disinfected before use. Whenever possible, equipment should be removed from food areas for repair.

Pests and pest control

Rodents, rodent hairs and droppings may be brought into food premises with the raw materials or introduced during the preparation or storage of food in infested premises. Food showing evidence of rodent contamination is unfit and should be rejected.

Insects, larvae and eggs may also be present in raw materials, although some may find their way into food rooms via openings. Several types of insect multiply rapidly and infestations can soon spread throughout food premises. Infested food should be discarded and appropriate control measures introduced. A reputable pest control contractor, experienced at working with food businesses, should be employed to lay rodent bait or traps and control pest infestations should they arise.

Bad pest control is likely to result in food contamination. For example, electronic fly killers positioned above open food, work surfaces or containers will probably result in dead insects in the food, as will the use of insecticides to destroy flying insects, for example, sprays, in the presence of open food.

Cleaners and other staff must be instructed not to touch bait boxes, unless authorized to do so, and never to put bait boxes on shelves above open products whilst cleaning is being undertaken.

Electronic fly killer exposing clean food containers to risk of contamination

Customer contamination

Customers may contaminate food which is not adequately protected, especially when they serve themselves. Handling and sneezing over food is probable and inquisitive customers may break seals to examine the contents of jars and tubs. Furthermore, malicious tampering of products in supermarkets continues to pose a threat to manufacturers and retailers. Finally, contamination of the product may occur in the consumer's home and this should be considered when investigating a complaint.

All reasonable precautions and all due diligence

A food company facing a prosecution as a result of selling a contaminated product will need to demonstrate that they have installed and used an effective, documented detection and rejection system, which is checked regularly, if they are to successfully use the 'due diligence' defence provided in food safety legislation. It will be up to the courts to decide what is 'reasonable' having regard to good trade practice, industry hygiene guides and the risk and consequences in relation to cost.

Foreign body detection and removal in food manufacturing

No system can guarantee to remove every contaminant and the effectiveness of a particular machine or system will depend on the type of foreign body, the initial level of contamination and the maintenance of the equipment. The performance of most machines will deteriorate with age and use and constant testing is essential. There are many contaminant detection and removal systems available including:
- metal detection systems;
- X-ray systems;
- sieves and filtration;
- optical systems, including colour sorters and scanners;
- magnets;
- air or liquid separation systems; and
- the use of operatives, for example, as spotters, on bottle lines or illuminated inspection belts.

CHEMICAL CONTAMINATION

Unwanted chemicals can enter foodstuffs during:

- growth, for example, veterinary drugs, fertilizers, pesticides and environmental contaminants such as lead or dioxins;
- processing or food preparation, for example, oil, cleaning chemicals or insecticides;
- transport, as a result of spillage or leakage; and
- sale, for example, cleaning chemicals, insecticides and leaking of such things as plasticizers from packaging. Chemicals may cause acute poisoning or cause long-term illnesses such as cancer.

Cleaning chemicals

To avoid taint, some cleaning chemicals, such as phenols and perfumed soap, must not be used in food premises, especially by those handling dairy/fatty foods. All cleaning materials must be kept in properly labelled containers and stored in a manner which obviates any risk of contamination.

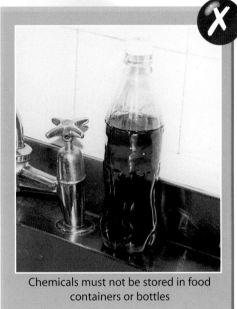

Chemicals must not be stored in food containers or bottles

Key points

- Contamination is a major hazard and may be considered as any objectionable matter in or on food.
- There are three types of contamination: microbiological, foreign bodies and chemicals.
- Sources of food poisoning bacteria include people, raw foods, pests and the environment.
- Vehicles of contamination include hands, cloths and equipment, hand-contact surfaces and food-contact surfaces.
- Routes are the path bacteria take when being transferred from sources to high-risk food.
- Routes can be disrupted by good design, good practice and cleaning and disinfection.
- Physical contamination results from packaging, the building and equipment, notices, food handlers, cleaning activities, pests and customer contamination
- All reasonable precautions and all due diligence should be taken to avoid prosecution as a result of the sale of contaminated food.
- Chemical contamination can occur during growth, processing/preparation, transport or sale.

4 *Food poisoning and foodborne disease*

Food poisoning is an acute illness which usually occurs within one to 36 hours of eating contaminated or poisonous food. Symptoms normally last from one to seven days and may include diarrhoea, vomiting, abdominal pain, nausea, fever and prostration.

Food poisoning may be caused by:

♦ bacteria or their toxins;
♦ poisonous fish, including scombrotoxic fish poisoning;
♦ chemicals such as insecticides, excessive additives and fungicides;
♦ metals such as lead, copper and mercury;
♦ poisonous plants such as deadly nightshade, toadstools; and
♦ moulds (mycotoxins).

Bacteria are responsible for most food poisoning cases, with poisonous fish, plants, chemicals or metals occasionally causing problems. Mycotoxins rarely cause illness in the UK. Viral gastroenteritis is very common but is dealt with as a foodborne disease: Viruses don't multiply in food and only a few viruses are needed to cause illness.

Causative agent (organism)

The causative agent is the bacteria, toxin or poison that contaminates the food and causes food poisoning when the food is consumed.

Onset or incubation period

The onset period is the time between consuming the contaminated food and the first signs of illness.

The food vehicle

The food vehicle is the food consumed that contains the causative agent.

The source

The source is the point from which the causative agent first enters the specific food chain, for example, a cow or a hen. It may also be considered to be the vehicle that brings the causative agent into the food premises responsible for the outbreak, for example, a person, raw milk or an egg.

IMPORTANT FOOD POISONING BACTERIA

Salmonella

Sources

The intestines of ill people and carriers, animals and animal food, raw meat, raw poultry, raw milk, raw eggs, pets, rodents, terrapins, faeces, flies, insects and sewage/water.

Common food vehicles

Undercooked or contaminated cooked meat and poultry, raw milk, raw eggs and uncooked foods using raw eggs in their preparation, for example, mayonnaise, mousses and tiramisu, cut lemon, bean sprouts, dried coconut, salad vegetables and chocolate.

Onset period

6 to 72 hours, usually 12 to 36 hours. Endotoxin in intestine (infective food poisoning).

Symptoms and duration of illness

Abdominal pain, diarrhoea, nausea, vomiting, fever and headache. The duration is usually one to seven days. Occasionally deaths are recorded usually involving the elderly, the very young and people who are already ill.

Specific characteristics

Usually requires millions of bacteria to cause illness. However, outbreaks involving low numbers have been recorded in food vehicles with high fat content, such as chocolate, milk and cheese. In such cases the incubation period may be upto 10 days. Salmonella multiplies from 7°C to 47°C under aerobic or anaerobic conditions.

Specific control measures

- Sterilize animal feed and avoid subsequent contamination.
- Segregate ill animals.
- Hygienic transport from farm to abattoir (avoid overcrowding).
- Hygienic slaughtering.
- Prevent cross-contamination between raw and high-risk food from storage through to serving.
- Complete thawing of frozen poultry.
- Thorough cooking to above 75°C. Use heat-treated milk.
- Double-wash raw, ready-to-eat salads and fruit.
- High standards of personal hygiene, especially handwashing after visiting the toilet and before handling high-risk food.
- Exclude symptomatic food handlers.
- Effective cleaning and disinfection.
- Chlorination of water.
- Safe sewage disposal.
- Exclude pests and animals from food premises or food contact.

Clostridium perfringens

Sources

Intestines of humans and animals, faeces and sewage, soil, dust, insects, raw meat and poultry.

Common food vehicles

Rolled joints, casseroles, stews, sauces, mince and meat pies when cooking has removed oxygen.

Onset period

8 to 22 hours, usually 12 to 18 hours. Enterotoxin produced in the intestines. Infective food poisoning.

Symptoms and duration of illness

Abdominal pain and diarrhoea. Vomiting is rare. Symptoms usually last 12 to 48 hours.

Specific characteristics

Clostridium multiplies between 10°C and 52°C under anaerobic conditions. The optimum temperature is between 43°C and 47°C. At 46°C *Clostridium perfringens* can double every ten minutes. It produces spores which can survive high temperatures and dehydration. Illness usually results from consuming millions of organisms. Spores germinate as a result of normal cooking temperatures and long, slow cooling allows the vegetative bacteria to multiply rapidly.

Specific control measures

♦ Separate raw and high-risk foods, especially meat and vegetables.
♦ Use ready prepared and washed root vegetables to avoid bringing soil into the kitchen. Double wash salad vegetables such as lettuce.
♦ Strict temperature control.
♦ Cook or reheat food to at least 75°C and then serve immediately or store above 63°C.
♦ Maximum joint sizes 2.25 kg.
♦ Rapidly cool joints, sauces, pies, etc. especially between 60°C and 20°C and then refrigerate.
♦ High standards of personal hygiene, especially handwashing after visiting the toilet and before handling high-risk food.
♦ Exclude symptomatic food handlers.
♦ Effective cleaning and disinfection.

Staphylococcus aureus

Sources

Human nose, mouth, skin, hands, boils, scratches, spots and cuts, especially if septic. Raw milk from cows or goats with mastitis, or products such as cheese made from raw milk. Up to 40% of the population may carry *Staphylococcus aureus* in their mouth or nose and upto 15% on their hands.

Common food vehicles

Milk and dairy products, trifles and cream desserts, custard-type products, cold cooked meat and poultry, salads, peeled cooked prawns, lasagne and fermented sausage.

Onset period

One to seven hours. Heat resistant exotoxin produced in food. Toxic food poisoning.

Symptoms and duration of illness

Abdominal pain, nausea, mainly vomiting, diarrhoea, collapse and occasionally subnormal temperatures. The duration is usually between 6 and 24 hours.

Specific characteristics

Sporadic cases may be common but are rarely notified and are not recorded. Staphylococcus multiplies in aerobic or anaerobic conditions between 7°C and 48°C. Can tolerate relatively high salt content. Usually requires millions of organisms to produce sufficient toxin to cause illness. Is usually harmless when not in food. Toxin may survive boiling for up to 30 minutes.

Specific control measures

- ♦ High standards of personal hygiene, especially handwashing before, and frequently whilst, handling high-risk food and not touching the mouth, nose or hair during food preparation.
- ♦ Avoid handling high-risk food, where possible use utensils.
- ♦ Exclude food handlers with respiratory infections especially those involving coughing or sneezing; boils or septic cuts; or skin infections that encourage scratching or flaking.
- ♦ Avoid consuming raw milk or products made from raw milk.
- ♦ Prevent cross-contamination (it may be present on chicken skin).
- ♦ Cover cuts with waterproof dressings.
- ♦ Strict temperature control of high-risk food.
- ♦ Precool salad ingredients.

Bacillus cereus

Sources

Cereals, especially rice, cornflour, dried food, spices, dust, vegetation, soil and intestinal tract of humans.

Common food vehicles

Reheated rice, cornflour products, foods containing spices, vanilla slices, custards, cream pastries, soups, vegetables dishes, meats and starchy foods, e.g. pasta and potatoes.

Onset period

Usually one to five hours. Exotoxin in food, which can survive temperatures of 126°C for up to 1.5 hours. Toxic food poisoning.

Symptoms and duration of illness

Nausea, vomiting, abdominal pain and some diarrhoea. The duration is usually 12 to 24 hours.

Specific characteristics

Bacillus cereus is a spore former, which produces an exotoxin in food and multiplies under aerobic or anaerobic conditions. Both the spores and the exotoxin will survive normal cooking temperatures. Millions of organisms are usually required to cause illness and bacteria multiply between 7°C and 48°C with an optimum between 28°C and 35°C. There is a second type of *Bacillus cereus*, which resembles *Clostridium perfringens* in that it produces a toxin in the intestine. The onset period is eight to 16 hours and symptoms are primarily abdominal pain and diarrhoea with some vomiting and fever.

Specific control measures
- Rapidly cool cooked food and store under refrigeration.
- Cooking must be thorough and, if unavoidable, reheating should be carried out at least to 75°C. Eat immediately or hot hold above 63ºC.
- Particular care with rice which should never be reheated more than once.
- Avoid cross-contamination.

Clostridium botulinum

Sources
Soil, vegetables, intestinal tract of fish and mammals.

Common food vehicles
Low-acid processed food, vacuum packed meat or fish, smoked or fermented fish, bottled vegetables, products containing spices, garlic oil, mascarpone cheese and dried milk.

Onset period
Two hours to eight days but usually 12 to 36 hours. A heat-sensitive neurotoxin produced in the food. (Affects the nervous system). Toxic food poisoning.

Symptoms and duration of illness
Difficulties in swallowing, talking and breathing. Double vision and muscular paralysis. Diarrhoea at first, followed by constipation. Fatalities are common and survivors may take several months to recover.

Specific characteristics
Clostridium botulinum multiplies between 3.3°C and 50°C under anaerobic conditions. Heat resistant spores are produced and the safety of canned food is based on the destruction of these spores, i.e. 121°C for a minimum of three minutes (botulinum cook).

Specific control measures
- Prevent post-process contamination of cans or vacuum packs of low-acid food.
- Ensure time/temperature combinations used in canning will destroy any spores of *Clostridium botulinum* that may be present.
- Do not use blown cans or cans with badly damaged seams.
- Use of preservatives such as nitrite in vacuum packs of meat.
- Thorough cooking of food immediately prior to consumption will probably destroy any toxin that is in the food.

- Smoked fish should be produced in accordance with good manufacturing practices and preferably stored in a freezer to prevent multiplication and toxin production.
- Strict attention to the shelf-life of vacuum packs.
- Strict temperature control.

Generic control measures for most food poisoning organisms

- High standards of personal hygiene, especially handwashing and exclusion of symptomatic food handlers.
- Keep raw food and high-risk food separate at all stages of production, from delivery through to service. Prevent cross-contamination.
- Store high-risk foods below 5°C or above 63°C. Cool food rapidly and keep it out of the danger zone.
- Ensure food is thoroughly cooked to core temperatures above 75°C.
- Ensure effective cleaning and disinfection.
- Ensure effective pest control.
- Avoid consuming raw foods likely to be contaminated with food poisoning organisms, especially bivalves, milk and eggs.
- Implementation of HACCP.
- The effective food safety training of all persons who can influence food safety, especially managers, supervisors and high-risk food handlers.

Food vehicles

The foods most commonly involved in food poisoning outbreaks are:
- poultry (undercooked);
- cooked red meat and meat products;
- desserts;
- shellfish (usually raw) and fish (scrombrotoxin);
- salads, vegetables and fruit (usually low infective dose organisms);
- raw or undercooked egg products such as mayonnaise, mousse, and homemade ice cream; and
- milk (usually raw) and milk products.

CAUSAL FACTORS RELATING TO OUTBREAKS OF FOOD POISONING

- Preparation too far in advance and storage at ambient temperature.
- Inadequate cooling.
- Undercooking.
- Cross-contamination.
- Improper warm holding.
- Use of leftovers.
- Contaminated processed food including canned.
- Inadequate reheating.
- Inadequate thawing.
- Raw food consumed.
- Infected food handlers.
- Extra large quantities prepared.

More recently, Dr Richard North has been investigating the 'failure of management' as the most important reason for food poisoning, for example:

- ♦ failure to carry out a risk-assessment when there is a change of menu, ingredients or recipes;
- ♦ lack of contingency planning, for example, when the oven or refrigerator breaks down;
- ♦ communication – a failure of management, or head office, to provide the front-line staff with the correct information;
- ♦ management disincentives, for example, bonus paid in relation to the amount spent on cleaning or training;
- ♦ commercially driven misuse of equipment or premises, for example, overloading refrigerators or catering for numbers beyond the capacity;
- ♦ a failure to recognize potentially hazardous procedures of the operation, for example, colour-coded equipment all being washed in the same sink with no disinfection;
- ♦ failure to implement recommendations, following an earlier outbreak;
- ♦ failure to replace complex or time-consuming operations, for example, refrigerators positioned a considerable distance from workstations. This militates against small amounts of food being prepared, which results in temperature abuse;
- ♦ unrealistic demands placed on junior management or untrained staff; and
- ♦ the absence of routine planning and consistent procedures.

FOOD POISONING OUTBREAKS DEMONSTRATING MANAGEMENT FAILURES

Staphylococcus aureus

Ten people developed symptoms after eating rolls filled with egg mayonnaise. Three people were admitted to hospital. The filling had been made from hard-boiled eggs. After chopping, these eggs had been left overnight in a refrigerator which had been too warm, as a result of loss of refrigerant. The filled rolls had then been placed in a 'refrigerated' display counter which was non-operative, the ambient temperature being 25°C. The source of the outbreak was the food handler who had prepared the eggs and while suffering from a skin infection. Although a 'classic' outbreak involving contamination from a food handler and inadequate temperature control, the underlying cause was the lack of equipment maintenance. This contributed significantly to the outbreak. Management also failed to recognize the hazards of inadequate temperature control and failed to realise that a food handler with a skin condition could present a serious hazard.

Salmonella

A hospital outbreak resulted in the death of three people and 119 cases of food poisoning. The vehicle of infection was roast lamb which had been cooked the day before it was served and had been left covered with cloths in a hospital corridor because of the 'sultry evening'. Conditions were considered 'absolutely perfect for bacterial multiplication'. The total consignment of 25 joints of lamb had been pre-cooked because the ovens were being repaired the following day. The hospital refrigerators were not used because they were full of jellies which would not have set at room temperature. The coroner was 'satisfied' this was an isolated incident, when someone had not 'gone by the book'. At some stage the roast lamb had become contaminated and there had been a 'classic' failure of temperature control. However, the underlying cause was clearly the failure of management to plan for the contingency of the oven repairs and to make satisfactory alternative arrangements.

Clostridium perfringens

In a hospital outbreak, patients in one of six wards who were served with roast meat and gravy succumbed to *Clostridium perfringens* food poisoning. Unaccountably, none of the patients in the other wards suffered, even though they had apparently been served the same meal. On investigation, however, it transpired that the chef had run out of gravy towards the end of serving and had quickly made up additional stock from the stock pot, without having had time to cook the mixture thoroughly. Further investigation showed that ingredient planning had been deficient in that there had been no specific quantities set out for a given number of meals. Quantities prepared were left to the judgement of the chef who estimated what was needed on an ad hoc basis. There were no established procedures, written or otherwise.

Clostridium botulinum

In June 1989 a botulism outbreak affected 27 people and one person died. The implicated product was hazelnut yoghurt. The contamination was traced to the manufacturer of canned hazelnut puree used in the yoghurt. The manufacturer was more used to producing high-acid fruit purées, in which the acidity from the fruit suppressed the growth of botulinum bacteria. However, he had employed the same process to make hazelnut purée. But this was a low-acid product, presenting a completely different order of risk. Changes to the ingredients were also made. Before the recipe had been changed, a full risk assessment should have been carried out.

Chemical food poisoning

Some chemicals are extremely poisonous and if ingested may result in a burning sensation in the mouth, severe vomiting and abdominal pain within a few minutes and occasional diarrhoea. Chemicals can enter foodstuffs by leakage, spillage or other accidents during processing or preparation. Unacceptable levels of benzene migration from plastic packaging and inappropriate use of fungicides have resulted in poisoning. However, acute chemical poisoning from food premises is rare and is usually caused by negligence, for example, storing weedkiller, pesticide or cleaning chemicals in unlabelled food containers.

Chemical additives of food have to undergo rigorous tests before they are allowed and are usually harmless. However, some may cause problems if ingested in large amounts, for example, three persons became ill after consuming sausages containing sodium nitrate and sodium nitrite at levels of 200 times that permitted for cured meats. Symptoms included drowsiness, dizziness and a greying colour of the skin.

Residues of drugs, pesticides and fertilizers may be present in deliveries of raw materials. Pesticides sprayed on to fruit and vegetables just prior to harvesting may result in cumulative toxic effects and should be strictly controlled. Approximately 20,000 Spanish people became ill after using olive oil sold by street vendors, which allegedly contained industrial waste oil. At least 350 people died.

Metallic food poisoning

Several metals are toxic and if ingested in sufficient quantities can give rise to food poisoning. The symptoms, mainly vomiting and abdominal pain, usually develop within an hour. Diarrhoea may also occur. Metals may be absorbed by growing crops, or contaminate food during processing. Acid foods, such as fruit, should not be cooked or stored in equipment containing: antimony (enamel coatings); cadmium (refrigeration apparatus); copper (pans); lead (ceramics, earthenware and lead crystal) or zinc (galvanized metals). Soft water may absorb lead from old pipes.

Tin and Iron

Acid foods may also cause problems if stored in tin-plated iron cans for too long. The acid foods react with the tin-plate and hydrogen gas is produced. Iron and tin are absorbed by the food which may become unfit for human consumption.

Poisonous plants

Poisonous plants are rarely the cause of food poisoning in food premises. Plants responsible for causing acute poisoning include deadly nightshade, death cap (which may be mistaken for edible mushroom) daffodil bulbs and rhubarb leaves.

Red kidney beans or haricot beans which are consumed raw or undercooked occasionally result in food poisoning. Nausea, vomiting and abdominal pain are likely within one to six hours of consuming the beans. Temperatures of canning will destroy the toxin.

Poisonous fish

The gonads, liver and intestines of some fish are highly toxic, for example, the puffer fish. Several incidents of red whelk poisoning have been recorded in the UK, due to a poison present in the salivary glands of these whelks. Symptoms include tingling of the fingers, disturbance of vision, paralysis, nausea, vomiting, diarrhoea and prostration.

Scombrotoxic fish poisoning

Scombrotoxic fish poisoning is caused by toxins which accumulate in the body of some fish, including tuna, mackerel, sardines, pilchards, herring, anchovies and salmon, during storage, especially above 4°C. The onset period is between ten minutes and three hours. Symptoms last up to eight hours and include headache, nausea, vomiting, abdominal pain, a rash on the face and neck, a burning or peppery sensation in the mouth, sweating and diarrhoea. Problems arise in canning fish as, once formed, the toxin is very heat-resistant and will not be destroyed during processing. Refrigerated storage of fish should prevent toxin formation.

Paralytic shellfish poisoning (PSP) and diarrhetic shellfish poisoning (DSP)

PSP and DSP may result from the consumption of mussels and other bivalves which have fed on poisonous plankton. The aquatic biotoxins causing PSP and DSP may withstand cooking. Symptoms of PSP include a tingling or numbness of the mouth almost immediately and this spreads to the neck, arms and legs within four to six hours. Death, when it does occur, is usually caused by respiratory paralysis within two to twelve hours. DSP symptoms include nausea, vomiting, abdominal pain, diarrhoea and chills with an onset time of thirty minutes to twelve hours.

FOODBORNE DISEASES

Foodborne diseases may be considered to differ from food poisoning in that:
- a relatively small number of organisms is capable of causing the illness;
- the food acts purely as a vehicle and the multiplication of the organism within the food is not an important feature of the illness;
- vehicles other than food may transmit the organism via the faecal-oral route;
- person-to-person spread and airborne transmission is more likely; and
- the incubation period is usually longer.

Viral gastroenteritis

Incidents of gastroenteritis are being increasingly attributed to viruses and undoubtedly contribute to a large number of notified cases of 'food poisoning'. However, viruses are predominantly infections of children and are rarely incriminated in foodborne transmission. Outbreaks in institutions and other 'closed' communities are common.

Noroviruses, previously known as Norwalk-like viruses (NLVs), are the major cause of viral foodborne cases and outbreaks in the UK. The onset period is usually around 12 to 48 hours and is dose dependent. The infective dose is very low, between ten and 100 organisms. Symptoms include vomiting, the predominant symptom and usually projectile, some diarrhoea, abdominal pain, fever and nausea. Symptoms usually last around 12 to 60 hours and patients are infectious for a further two days.

Viruses are around 3/100ths the size of bacteria and can only be seen through an electron microscope. They multiply in living cells not in food. Transmission depends on contamination of food by food handlers or sewage. Filter feeding bivalves, such as oysters harvested from sewage-polluted waters, are a major problem. Foods which are handled the most present the greatest risk; ice, desserts, cold meats, salads and some fruits are frequently involved, but the vehicle is rarely identified.

The virus is present in vomit and airborne infection and person-to-person spread often occurs. Re-infection is common. Viruses thrive in cold conditions and are destroyed at temperatures above 60°C. Relaying of shellfish in clean water is ineffective against viral contamination.

Control measures include staff training, the exclusion of ill food handlers, the implementation of HACCP, effective cleaning and disinfection of surfaces and equipment, the use of reputable suppliers and the washing/blanching of fruit and salads.

Typhoid and paratyphoid fever

Sometimes known as enteric fever, typhoid is caused by the bacterium *Salmonella* Typhi and paratyphoid by the bacterium *Salmonella* Paratyphi. The incubation period is normally between one and three weeks. Symptoms include fever, malaise, slow pulse, spleen enlargement, rose spots on the trunk and constipation or severe diarrhoea. The fatality rate for typhoid is between 2% and 10%. Paratyphoid is generally much less severe and symptoms may be similar to food poisoning caused by salmonella.

The organism is excreted in the faeces and urine of patients and carriers. Enteric fever may be waterborne, due to contamination by sewage, or foodborne, for example, milk or cooked meat contaminated by polluted water or by carriers who are food handlers. Laboratory confirmation is by bacteriological examination of blood, faeces or urine.

Control measures

♦   Using approved suppliers.
♦   Ensuring the safety of all water supplies. Water used for food preparation or drinking should be chlorinated.
♦   Ensuring the satisfactory disposal of sewage.
♦   Ensuring the heat treatment of milk and milk products, including ice cream.
♦   Preventing the sale of raw shellfish from sewage-polluted waters.
♦   Identifying carriers and ensuring that they are not employed within the food industry. Medical questionnaires should be used as an aid to recruitment.
♦   Maintaining high standards of personal hygiene amongst food handlers, especially with regard to thorough handwashing after visiting the toilet.
♦   Ensuring high standards of hygiene in food production and distribution.
♦   Washing/blanching of fruits and vegetables.

Dysentery

In the UK, bacillary dysentery is usually caused by the bacterium *Shigella sonnei*. It is an acute disease of the intestine characterized by diarrhoea, fever, stomach cramps, nausea, and often vomiting. Stools may contain blood, mucus and pus. Fatality is normally less than 1%. The incubation period is usually around four days, although it varies between one and seven days. Dysentery is spread through faecal-oral transmission from an infected person or by the consumption of contaminated foods, including water and milk. Control measures are similar to those used for typhoid, with the emphasis on personal hygiene.

Campylobacter enteritis

Campylobacter jejuni is now the most frequently reported reason for acute bacterial diarrhoea. In 2004, around 42,000 faecal specimens submitted to laboratories in England and Wales tested positive for campylobacter and 4,365 in Scotland. However, high-risk food was only proven to be a vehicle for a few of these. The main vehicle has yet to be identified.

Symptoms include headache, fever, diarrhoea (often bloodstained), persistent colicky abdominal pain (may mimic acute appendicitis) and nausea (vomiting is rare). The incubation period is usually between two and five days and the normal duration of illness is one to seven days.

Campylobacters disappear from the stools within a few weeks of illness and long-term carriers have not been detected. Animals and wild birds are the main source and as campylobacters can survive in water for several weeks, untreated water is a potential source. Campylobacters are commonly found on raw poultry, in raw milk and sewage and on carcase meat and offal.

Transmission is thought to be from raw and undercooked poultry and meat, raw milk, bottled milk pecked by birds, especially magpies, contaminated water (private supplies) and infected dogs and cats. Person-to-person spread and secondary cases are rare. Cross-contamination from raw poultry is extremely likely and hands can carry campylobacters for up to an hour. Campylobacters multiply quickly between 37°C and 43°C but not below 28°C. The organisms may be destroyed by heating food to 60°C for 15 minutes and are sensitive to drying. Illness can be caused by less than 500 organisms.

Control measures include reducing the numbers of campylobacters in raw meat and the food chain, hygiene training of food handlers, especially on the dangers of cross-contamination and the importance of thorough cooking, and also raising the hygiene awareness of consumers. Milk should be heat treated and water chlorinated.

Listeriosis

Although food is not the only means of transmission, and in the majority of cases a food vehicle is not identified, listeriosis is considered to be a foodborne illness. It is caused by *Listeria monocytogenes*, which is widely distributed in the environment. It is commonly found in effluents and sewage sludge and survives many weeks after spraying. In one outbreak involving coleslaw, the cabbage, stored for several months, had been grown in a field fertilized by sheep manure. The bacteria may be excreted by human or animal carriers, and many cases of cross-infection have been recorded. Symptoms are flu-like and include fever, diarrhoea, vomiting, septicaemia, meningitis and abortion; neonates, pregnant women, immuno-suppressed persons and the elderly are most at risk. The incubation period is one to 70 days.

A death rate of up to 30% is possible but mainly involves persons with other serious illness. The Government has issued warnings to at-risk groups to avoid soft cheeses, cook-chill meals and paté, although small numbers of listeria can be found in most foods from time to time.

Escherichia coli O157

Most *E. coli* that are found in the intestine are harmless. However, *E. coli* O157 causes serious illness, which is sometimes fatal, particularly in young children and the elderly. Symptoms vary from a watery diarrhoea, nausea and abdominal pain to bright red bloody diarrhoea and severe abdominal cramps, usually without fever. Up to 30% of patients develop haemolytic uraemic syndrome (HUS). This generally involves young children and *E. coli* O157 is the major cause of acute renal failure in children in the UK. Fatality rates range from 1% to 5%, but in some outbreaks, for example, involving the elderly, may be much higher. The incubation period is one to 14 days, with a median of three to four days. The duration of illness is approximately two weeks, unless complications, such as HUS, develop. *E. coli* O157 disappears from adult faeces within a few days.

Although *E. coli* O157 can multiply in food, it has a very low infective dose involving less than 100 bacteria. Infection results from eating contaminated foods, person-to-person spread and direct contact with animals, especially farm animals and their faeces. The main food vehicles are undercooked meat products, especially burgers and mince, contaminated cooked meat, vegetables fertilized with manure and unwashed, contaminated fruit. Other foods implicated include raw milk, cheese made with unpasteurized milk and apple juice. However, because of the low infective dose, cross-contamination of many ready-to-eat foods from raw meat is likely to result in illness. The main reservoir of *E. coli* O157 is the stomach and intestines of cattle and, possibly, sheep. It survives and multiplies in some foods at ambient temperatures, although numbers may decline at 4°C. It is destroyed by normal, effective cooking processes. Most outbreak investigations fail to identify a food vehicle.

Hepatitis A

Infectious hepatitis is a viral infection with an abrupt onset. Symptoms include fever, malaise, nausea, abdominal pain and later jaundice. The incubation period is 15 to 50 days and the duration one week to several months. Man is the reservoir and transmission is by the faecal-oral route. Faeces, blood and urine may be infected and can contaminate food, especially water, shellfish and milk.

Control measures are similar to those used for typhoid. A temperature of 90°C for 90 seconds will inactivate the virus.

Parasites

A parasite is a plant or animal which lives on or in another plant or animal known as the host. The parasite obtains its food from the host. They often have complicated life cycles which may involve different hosts. For example, tapeworms, such as *Taenia saginata* live in man, whereas the eggs are eaten by grazing cattle and develop in the muscle of cattle. If undercooked infected beef is eaten, the adult tapeworm develops in man. Parasites may be destroyed by cooking or by commercial freezing.

5 Personal hygiene

Food safety legislation requires:

♦ every person working in a food handling area to maintain a high standard of personal cleanliness, including wearing suitable, clean and, where appropriate, protective clothing;

♦ the supervision and instruction and/or training of food handlers in food hygiene matters commensurate with their work activity; and

♦ persons known or suspected to be suffering from, or carriers of, a disease likely to be transmitted through food, including infected wounds, skin infections or diarrhoea, must be excluded from food handling if there is a likelihood of contaminating food with pathogenic organisms.

Food handlers must, therefore, be in good health, have clean habits and be instructed or trained to ensure they do not contaminate food or allow food to become contaminated or maintained at ambient temperatures which are likely to promote the multiplication of food poisoning or spoilage bacteria.

Training of food handlers

Training involves the provision of knowledge and its implementation (practice) to ensure proficiency. Food handlers need to understand the controls, monitoring and corrective actions to be taken at points critical to food safety for which they are responsible. Thus food handlers involved with high-risk food preparation require more training than those only handling packaged or low-risk foods.

Food businesses require a planned training programme which includes induction, awareness and refresher training. The knowledge provided will depend on the risks and responsibilities associated with each job, knowledge may be provided by instruction, attending in-house or formal courses or from computer programmes. However, to be successful it is essential that there is

Food handlers must have high standards of personal hygiene.

commitment and support from directors and managers, effective supervision and adequate resources. High standards of food safety result when the culture of the business ensures good hygiene practices are implemented and rewarded.

Hazards from food handlers

Potential hazards arise from *Staphylococcus aureus* which is often present on the hands, in the nose or mouth and in spots and septic cuts. Cross-contamination is also probable if hands are not properly washed after touching raw meat, or other contaminated sources, before handling high-risk foods. A very serious hazard is presented if food handlers fail to wash their hands after using the toilet. The faecal-oral route is one of the main ways that low-dose pathogens (those organisms which only require a few to be present on food to make you ill), such as *E. coli* O157, *Shigella sonnei* or campylobacter result in illness. Persons with loose stools and carriers may be responsible for several serious outbreaks of foodborne illness because of poor personal hygiene.

Hands

Hands are the main vehicle for transferring food poisoning bacteria to high-risk food. For this reason, hands should be kept clean and washed frequently throughout the day and especially:

♦ after visiting the toilet (toilet paper is porous);
♦ on entering the food room, after a break, and before handling any food or equipment;
♦ after dealing with an ill customer or a baby's nappy;
♦ between handling raw food, such as poultry, red meat, eggs or shellfish, and handling ready-to-eat food;
♦ after changing or putting on a dressing;
♦ after cleaning up animal faeces (guide dog or guard dog) or handling boxes contaminated with bird droppings;
♦ after combing or touching the hair, nose, mouth or ears;
♦ after eating, smoking, coughing or blowing the nose;
♦ after handling external packaging or flowers;
♦ after handling waste food or refuse; and
♦ after cleaning, or handling dirty cloths, crockery etc.

The correct handwashing procedure is essential. Around 3 to 5ml of liquid soap should be applied to wet hands. A good lather should be produced by rubbing the hands and fingertips together. Between the fingers, around the thumbs, the fingertips and wrists should be thoroughly lathered for about 20 seconds. The lather should be rinsed off in warm flowing water at around 43°C. Efficient drying of the hands with a clean disposable paper towel will reduce the number of bacteria even more. A paper towel may be used to turn off the tap. Sufficient lather, friction and warm running water are the essential features to removing transient bacteria from the hands.

A soft nailbrush must be used to remove bacteria from the fingertips and under the fingernails after using the toilet, cleaning up vomit or faecal material, changing a dressing or handling raw poultry or meat before handling high-risk food. Excessive use of a stiff nailbrush and bactericidal soap both increase the risk of dermatitis. Gloves are often defective or abused and not necessary in most food handling situations. If disposable gloves are used in very high-risk situations the hands should be washed before putting on the gloves and after taking them off. The gloves should be discarded frequently and immediately if damaged.

As fingernails may harbour dirt and bacteria, they must be kept short and clean. False nails should not be worn. Nail varnish may chip and contaminate food and should not be used. Persons who continually put their fingers in their mouth, for example, nail-biters should not be employed as food handlers. Keeping the skin in good condition will reduce the likelihood of harbouring *Staphylococcus aureus* bacteria in cracks.

As far as practicable, the best policy is to avoid handling food by using hygienic utensils and equipment, such as serving tongs, trays and plates which are carried by the rim. Furthermore, the hands should not come into contact with the parts of the glasses, cups, spoons, etc. that will end up in a customer's mouth.

The nose, mouth and ears

Up to 40% of adults carry *Staphylococcus aureus* in their nose. Coughs and sneezes can carry droplet infection for considerable distances and contaminate food and/or work surfaces. Persons with bad colds should not handle open food. Hands should be washed after blowing the nose and single-use disposable paper handkerchiefs are preferred.

As the mouth is also likely to harbour *Staphylococcus aureus*, food handlers should not eat sweets, chew gum, taste food with fingers or a previously used spoon, or blow into glasses to polish them. Spitting is obviously prohibited as is nose and teeth picking or poking fingers into the ears.

Discharges from the ears, eyes and nose may contaminate food and such ailments must be reported to the supervisor. Medical clearance will normally be required before resuming work.

Cuts, boils, septic spots and skin infections

Food handlers with boils and septic lesions should be excluded from high-risk food handling areas as they will be infected with *Staphylococcus aureus*. All wounds should be completely protected by a conspicuously coloured waterproof dressing. Blue dressings are used to improve their visibility in food if they fall off. Loose dressings should be replaced immediately. Loss of dressings must be reported immediately to the supervisor.

Cuts on hands may need the extra protection of waterproof fingerstalls. Waterproof dressings are necessary to prevent blood and bacteria contaminating the food and to prevent bacteria from food, especially raw meat or fish, infecting the wound which may turn septic. Furthermore, waterproof dressings do not collect grease and dirt. Metal strips incorporated in dressings assist detection only where metal detectors are in use.

Staff who report for work wearing unacceptable dressings must have them changed before they enter a food room or commence food handling duties.

First aid

Food businesses must have a suitable and sufficient supply of first aid materials. One person should be given the responsibility of ensuring adequate provisions are always available. It is advisable to have at least one person trained in first aid and this may be a legal requirement.

The hair

Hair is constantly falling out and, along with dandruff, can result in contamination of food products by bacteria, especially *Staphylococcus aureus*. The hair should be shampooed regularly and completely enclosed by suitable head covering. Hairnets worn under hats and helmets are recommended. Combing of hair and adjustment of head covering should only take place in cloakrooms and should not be carried out whilst wearing protective clothing, as hairs may end up on the shoulders and then in the food. Hair grips and clips may also contaminate food and should never be worn outside the head covering. Scratching of the head should be avoided.

Jewellery and perfume

Food handlers should not wear earrings, watches, jewelled rings or brooches as they harbour dirt and bacteria. Furthermore, stones and small pieces of metal are a potential physical hazard. They may end up in the food and result in a customer complaint. Strong-smelling perfume, handcreams or aftershave are a potential chemical hazard and should not be worn by the food handlers as they may taint the food, especially food with a high fat content.

Smoking

Smoking and the use of tobacco is prohibited in food rooms or whilst handling open food because:

- ♦ of the danger of contaminating food from fingers which touch the lips and may transfer bacteria to food;
- ♦ cigarette ends contaminated with saliva are placed on working surface;
- ♦ cigarette ends and ash may contaminate the food;

Notices should not be ignored

- ♦ it encourages coughing; and
- ♦ an unpleasant environment may be created for non-smokers.

Legible notices should be displayed instructing food handlers who need to smoke to use specified locations and never to smoke in the food rooms.

Protective clothing

All food handlers should wear clean, washable, light-coloured, easy-to-clean protective clothing, preferably without external pockets. Press studs or Velcro fastening are preferable to buttons. Protective garments should be appropriate for the work being carried out and should completely cover ordinary clothing. Jumper and shirt sleeves must not protrude and, if short-sleeved overalls are worn, only clean forearms must be visible. Staff must be aware that protective clothing is primarily worn to protect the food from risk of contamination and not to keep their own clothes clean. Outdoor clothing and personal effects must not be brought into food rooms. Dust, pet hairs and woollen fibres are just a few of the contaminants carried on ordinary clothing. Lockers for outdoor clothing should be provided in non-food rooms.

The correct procedure must always be followed when putting on protective clothing. Head covering should always be put on first, followed by coats or boiler suits to avoid hairs getting on to the shoulders of protective clothing. Protective head covering should not be removed at breaks unless the protective overall or coat is removed first. Protective clothing should not be kept in toilets and, if practical, should be removed prior to using the toilet. Protective clothing should not be worn outside the food premises, not used to travel to and from work and not worn during lunch time sporting activities such as football or lying on the grass.

The use of different coloured protective clothing is recommended to distinguish between staff who handle only raw food and those who handle high-risk food. In addition, disposable protective clothing is becoming more widely available.

Aprons, if worn, should be suitable for the particular operation, light-coloured and capable of being thoroughly cleaned or disposable. Aprons which are torn or have badly-worn surfaces which create cleaning difficulties should be replaced. Facilities should be provided for cleaning waterproof aprons at various times during production and at the end of each working day. Cleanable hooks should be provided for hanging up aprons.

Suitable footwear should be worn to prevent slipping and to protect the feet. Boots may be provided for wearing in wet areas. They should be anti-slip, unlined and easy to clean. Suitable facilities should be provided for cleaning and storing cleaned boots.

Exclusion of food handlers

Supervisors must be aware that apparently healthy, symptom-free employees may be carriers of, and excrete, pathogenic bacteria. Laboratory testing cannot be relied on to detect small numbers of intermittently excreted pathogens. High standards of hygiene are therefore the only way to prevent the contamination of food by an infected food handler. It is a legal requirement for food handlers to advise their supervisor if they are suffering from diarrhoea or vomiting and/or suspect they may be carrying a food poisoning organism.

Food handlers with food poisoning symptoms, such as diarrhoea or vomiting, or suspected of carrying foodborne organisms, e.g., because of close contact with a confirmed case of typhoid or consuming a meal known to have caused illness, must be excluded from any job which would expose food to risk of contamination. Where appropriate, the Environmental Health Department should be informed immediately so that an environmental health officer can carry out urgent investigations. The guidance from the Department of Health, 'Food Handlers: Fitness to Work' states that any person who is excreting food poisoning organisms must not be allowed to engage in food handling until they have been free of symptoms for 48 hours, once any treatment has ceased, and have received medical clearance. However, it is critical that good hygiene, particularly handwashing, is observed.

If the supervisor has no confidence in the hygiene standards of a food handler who is a carrier of a food poisoning organism, even when symptom-free for 48 hours, they should not be allowed to handle high-risk food.

Food handlers returning from holidays abroad, particularly from countries with warm climates and suspect sanitation, should complete a short medical questionnaire. Even if they have fully recovered from symptoms of diarrhoea or vomiting experienced on holiday, they should be excluded from food handling until they have provided at least one negative specimen.

Food handlers with skin infections such as psoriasis, boils or septic cuts, respiratory tract infections, infection of the eyes or ears, dental sepsis or purulent gingivitis must also be excluded until medical clearance has been obtained.

Key points

♦ Most food handlers will carry food poisoning organisms at one time or another.

♦ High standards of personal hygiene are essential to avoid contamination of food.

♦ Hygiene training of food handlers will assist in the prevention of food poisoning.

♦ Frequent handwashing is essential.

♦ Cuts should be protected with brightly coloured waterproof dressings.

♦ Food should be handled as little as possible.

♦ Food handlers who are suffering from or are suspected of carrying infections, which may contaminate food, should be excluded until medical clearance has been received.

6 *The storage and temperature control of food*

The storage of food is important to ensure adequate provision throughout the year and to overcome fluctuations in supply. However, failure to ensure satisfactory conditions of temperature, humidity, stock rotation and the integrity of packaging can result in problems of unfit or spoiled food and will, at the very least, result in a considerable reduction in shelf-life. Inadequate temperature control is the most common cause of food poisoning. Correct storage and good temperature control is therefore crucial to food safety.

Raw materials

Most raw food of animal origin, shellfish, vegetables, spices and some fruits may be contaminated with pathogenic microorganisms and should be considered as potentially hazardous. Inadequate cooking/processing or cooling, and contamination of high-risk foods from raw foods are common causes of food poisoning. Therefore, food premises must have adequate and suitable storage facilities to keep all raw materials satisfactorily. Furthermore, the quality and bacteriological condition of raw materials has a significant influence on the finished product. Unsatisfactory deliveries may introduce problems such as insects, rodents or mould into the production area.

To assist in demonstrating due diligence, should the need arise, and to ensure that deliveries meet the agreed specification, effective, documented checking systems are advisable. Systems required will depend on the type of product and the condition of other deliveries from the same source. Checks may include: quantity, temperature, date code and quality – with particular emphasis on damaged or discoloured packaging.

Perishable food must be checked quickly and removed to cold stores, freezers or refrigerators without delay. Unloading of vehicles should take place, as far as practicable, in covered bays screened from adverse weather. Raw food and high-risk food should be completely segregated to avoid risk of contamination. Non-food items and strong-smelling foods which may cause taint problems should normally be delivered separately. When unloading, batches of food should be clearly marked, if they do not already bear suitable markings, to ensure that they are used in strict rotation and to identify the date of delivery in the event of subsequent complaints.

Raw meat and poultry

Raw meat joints should be stored between -1°C and +1°C, with a relative humidity of around 90%. Joints should keep for up to a week, although processed raw meats and offals will have a shorter life. Products should not touch the wall surface. Only approved suppliers should be used.

Eggs

Eggs should be sourced from a reputable supplier and stored in a clean, dry place, at a constant temperature below 20°C (ideally between 10°C and 15°C) and used within three weeks of lay. Temperature fluctuations should be avoided. Stock rotation is essential and cracked or dirty eggs should be rejected.

Meat pies, pasties and sausage rolls

These products must be obtained from a reliable source and should preferably be stored under refrigeration. Temperatures of around 7°C, with good air movement, are recommended so that the pastry remains crisp. As these foods are cooked to temperatures as high as 90°C, very few bacteria survive. Consequently, they remain bacteriologically safe at higher refrigeration temperatures. However, stock rotation is important and such products should be sold on the day of production or the following day. Pies or pasties to which something has been added after baking should be stored at or below 5°C. Temperatures should be kept constant as fluctuations result in condensation and mould growth.

As these products may be consumed without further cooking they must never be stored with raw meat or vegetables. Strong-smelling foods, such as cheese, may introduce taint or mould problems. Price tickets must not be stuck into pies or any other food. If pies are to be sold hot from retail outlets they must be cooked thoroughly and, if stored, maintained above 63°C. Alternatively, pies may be microwaved as required. They must never be re-warmed.

Fruit and vegetables

Although each fruit and vegetable has its own optimal storage conditions, a general guide is to keep them in a cool room or a refrigerator. However, tropical fruits such as pineapples and bananas should be stored at 10°C to 13°C to avoid 'chill injury'. Care must be taken to prevent warm moist conditions and condensation which will encourage bacterial spoilage and mould growth. Low humidities and excessive ventilation result in dehydration and must also be avoided. Fruit should be examined regularly and mouldy items removed to avoid rapid mould spread. Transit wrappings, especially 'non-breathing' plastic films, may need to be removed to avoid condensation.

Ice cream

Ice cream should be kept in clean, dedicated freezers. Ice cream must not be stored with raw products. It should always be kept frozen and discarded if defrosted. Tubs should be used completely before fresh tubs are started and nothing should be placed on top of open tubs. Lids should normally be kept on. The texture of ice cream is more temperature sensitive than other frozen foods and it may be held at -12°C before use.

Milk and cream

Milk and cream should be stored under refrigeration (below 5°C) and should be placed in the refrigerator or cold store as soon as received. Imitation cream should also be refrigerated. Crates of milk should not be stored below raw meat.

Flour and cereals

Large quantities of flour and cereals should preferably be stored in bulk containers. Lids must be tight-fitting. Large stocks of flour kept in original sacks must be stored clear of the ground and free from damp. Condensation may result in mould growth on wet flour and must be prevented. Regular cleaning of containers used for flour storage must not be overlooked. Frequent inspections, at least weekly, should be carried out for rodents or insects.

Canned foods

Canned goods should be examined regularly and blown or leaking cans must be rejected. They should be kept in cool, dry conditions. Acid foods should not be stored in opened cans within refrigerators, because of the acid attack, in the presence of oxygen, on the internal surface of the can. This can lead to metallic taint.

The shelf-life of canned foods

High-acid cans of fruit, such as prunes, rhubarb, tomatoes and strawberries, may blow if kept longer than recommended by the manufacturer. The acid juice attacks the tin and iron of the can, especially at the seams. Some large cans of meat, especially ham, may only have been pasteurized and therefore need to be refrigerated. If this is the case, the can will be clearly labelled.

On opening, can contents should be placed in a suitable plastic or stainless steel container, if not intended for immediate use. If the food is discoloured or has an unusual smell or texture, or the interior of the can is rusty or discoloured, the food must be rejected.

Wrapping and packaging

Packaging and wrapping materials must be stored in clean, dry areas where they are not exposed to risk of contamination.

Cling film

Cling film is useful for stopping food drying out and protecting it against contamination (special breathing films are available for raw meats). Under certain conditions, however, it can speed up spoilage and mould growth by trapping moisture. It is important therefore that:

♦ raw meat or wet food is unwrapped when removed from the refrigerator; and
♦ food wrapped in cling film is not left in bright light or sunlight.

Because of the risk of chemical migration, cling films should not be used where they could melt into food during heating, or for wrapping foods with a high fat content, unless manufacturer's advice indicates their suitability for this purpose.

Vacuum packing

Vacuum-packed food, and modified atmosphere packs, should be refrigerated, unless the labelling indicates otherwise. Immediately after opening a vacuum pack, the contents should be removed completely. Slightly darker colours of meat and the acid odour will disappear shortly after being removed.

Care must be taken to avoid puncturing packs, for example, with sharp bones or rough handling. Defective seams commonly result in the loss of pack integrity. However, air-tight vacuum packaging may blow if the contents ferment. It is advisable to purchase branded vacuum packs from reputable suppliers to avoid receiving low-grade meat of dubious origin. Unmarked packs without 'use-by' dates should always be regarded with suspicion.

Damaged stock

All damaged stock should be segregated and thoroughly examined before use. If there is any doubt regarding the fitness of food it should be discarded, or the local Environmental Health Department may be asked for advice.

The greenhouse effect

Food, especially high-risk food, should not be stored in windows or in glass display cabinets which are exposed to direct sunlight. The heat within the cabinet will build up in the same way that it does in a greenhouse, providing conditions ideal for bacterial multiplication. The greenhouse effect may even occur in chill cabinets without proper chilled air circulation, and fluorescent tubes may exaggerate the problem.

Stock rotation

Satisfactory rotation of stock, to ensure that older food is used first, is essential to avoid spoilage and unnecessary wastage. Stock rotation applies to all types of food. Daily checks should be made on short-life perishable food stored in refrigerators whereas weekly examination of other foods may suffice. Stock which is undisturbed for long periods will encourage pest infestations. The rule is: 'First in, first out'. Written stock control records are recommended and are useful to assist a 'due diligence' defence. Food should always be checked before use to ensure it is within date, in good condition and packaging is undamaged.

Codes

Stock rotation has been much easier since the advent of open-date coding but some products do not require a 'use-by' or 'best-before' date. In these cases, retailers should adopt their own code to identify the date of delivery. A colour code system is one of the easiest to use: a blue line for Monday; a red line for Tuesday; etc. A double coloured line should be used the following week. 'Use-by' dates are placed on perishable, short-life products, whereas 'best-before' dates are used on longer life products. Products with an expired 'use-by' date should be considered as unfit, whereas those products with an expired 'best-before' date are more likely to be of an unacceptable quality. The practice of selling old stock cheaply is not recommended. It is an offence to sell any food which is unfit or foods bearing an expired 'use-by' date or to change this date.

Dry-goods stores

Rooms used for the storage of fruit and vegetables, dried, canned and bottled foods should be kept dry, cool (preferably between 10°C and 15°C), well lit, and well ventilated. They must be kept clean and tidy and spillages should be cleared away promptly. Rodent and bird-proofing should be maintained and any gaps in the fabric should be sealed. As far as possible food should be kept in rodent-proof containers. All goods should be stored clear of walls and floors to allow cleaning and pest control.

Non-food items, including cleaning equipment and chemicals, and strong smelling foods should not be stored in dry-goods stores. Packs of food should be handled carefully to avoid damage. Part-used packs should be resealed to prevent contamination. Alternatively, food may be transferred to clean containers with pest-proof lids.

REFRIGERATORS

Refrigerators should be readily accessible, and sited clear of heat sources unless they are designed for high-temperature environments. Ideally they should be in well-ventilated areas away from the direct rays of the sun. Multi-deck, open display cabinets should be sited clear of draughts from doorways, and ventilation and heating grills fitted in ceilings, which may result in significant increase in temperatures. High humidities should be avoided, as these will cause condensation on stored foods. The siting of all units should permit the cleaning of surrounding areas as well as the cooling coils. Regular maintenance and defrosting (where not automatic) should be carried out and door seals checked.

Defective refrigerator door seals should be replaced

Cleaning should be frequent, taking in both exteriors, especially door handles, and interiors. Internal surfaces and fans should also be disinfected. Base plates and baffle plates should be removed to check for debris such as price tickets and packaging which can obstruct air flow and block drains in multi-deck units. Drip trays, if present, should be emptied and cleaned. Dust on evaporator coils and air ducts must be removed to maintain performance.

After cleaning and disinfection, units should be completely dried and brought to correct operating temperatures before being reloaded. Stock should be kept in back-up chill stores during cleaning operations. Food which experiences a significant increase in temperature, above 10°C for excessive time, due to breakdown or power cut should be destroyed.

Operating temperatures

The optimum temperature for multi-use refrigerators, in which high-risk foods are stored, is between 1°C and 4°C. Cook-chill foods with a maximum shelf-life of five days must be kept between 0°C and 3°C.

Hot food

Hot food, not intended for immediate consumption, should be cooled rapidly. It should not be placed directly into a refrigerator as this may raise the temperature of food already stored, as well as increasing the ice build-up on the cooling unit. Condensation may also occur on some foods, resulting in an unacceptable drip on to food stored below.

Ice build up on the cooling unit

However, depending on the amount of food and the capacity of the refrigerator, it may be preferable to place a small amount of food which has cooled to around 50°C into a large capacity unit instead of leaving it in a warm environment for prolonged periods or overnight.

Contamination

It is essential that precautions are taken to avoid contamination. Raw food must always be kept apart from high-risk food. It is recommended that separate, clearly labelled units be used. If only one refrigerator is available, high-risk food must be stored above raw food. Shelves previously used for raw foods must not be used for high-risk foods without cleaning and disinfection. All foods should be adequately covered to prevent drying out, cross-contamination and the absorption of odour.

Packing and rotation of food

Refrigerators should not be overloaded and they need packing in a manner which allows good air circulation. A gap of at least 3cm should always be allowed between trays stored on slatted shelves. Food should not be placed directly in front of the cooling unit as this reduces efficiency. Non-perishables should not be stored in a refrigerator if this takes up valuable space. Good stock rotation is essential, and daily checks should be made for out-of-date stock.

Staff responsibilities

Staff should be given clear instructions on how to use refrigerators. They should be instructed to open doors as little, and for as short a time, as possible. The temperature of the refrigerator should be checked at least three times per day and records of readings should be kept. Spillages should be cleared up immediately.

The storage life of perishable food under refrigeration

Shelf-life varies according to the operating temperature of the refrigerator and the specific perishable food. For example, at 1˚C, most vegetables will keep for at least two weeks, butter for two months and fresh beef up to a week.

Chilled display cabinets

Cabinets should be loaded correctly so that cold air inlets are not obstructed and load-lines are not exceeded. Only chilled products should be placed in display cabinets.

Radiant heat can have a significant effect on food stored in chilled cabinets, particularly on the upper shelves. Cabinets, therefore, should be sited away from heating units and high-intensity lights and out of direct sunlight.

Monitoring temperatures

Cabinet thermometer readings should be checked using an accurate digital or infrared thermometer. Indicating or recording thermometers are essential and premises with a large number of units will need automatic monitoring equipment and alarms to warn of unacceptable temperatures. If records indicate temperatures above prescribed limits, between-pack temperatures should be taken. If concern remains then probing of the food should be undertaken.

Infrared thermometers

Infrared thermometers, which work by measuring the amount of radiant energy, can be used to scan foods very rapidly. Any identified problems can be checked immediately with a digital thermometer. Additional advantages include the fact that it is non-destructive testing and there is no risk of cross-contamination. It is particularly useful for scanning retail cabinets, frozen food, deliveries and despatch as large consignments can be checked for hot spots.

Temperature data loggers

Data loggers and printers will provide a variety of useful information about refrigerated storage including current temperature, maximum, minimum and trends of temperature over a specified period. Should temperatures rise above a predetermined level they can also trigger an alarm.

Cooking

Cooking is used to make food palatable and safe for immediate consumption. Core temperatures of 75˚C are usually adequate to destroy food poisoning bacteria although some preformed toxins and spores will not be destroyed. Lower temperatures for longer times may be equally effective. A disinfected digital probe thermometer should be used to check correct core temperatures have been achieved, especially for poultry and rolled joints. Colour changes and 'juices of poultry running clear' are useful indicators of correct cooking.

Cooling of hot food

Rapid cooling of cooked foods to be chilled or frozen is extremely important to prevent spore germination or the multiplication of any surviving pathogens or those introduced. It is usually recommended that food is cooled below 10°C in less than 1.5 hours. Practically, only blast chillers can achieve this. A more pragmatic standard adopted by the Food and Drugs Authority in America is to cool joints from 60°C to 21°C in two hours and from 21°C to 7°C within a further four hours. Ice water baths cool faster than cold air.

When cooling food, the following basic rules should be applied:
- minimize bulk – the smaller the size of the food, the faster it will cool;
- maximize surface area – square or rectangular containers present greater surface areas than round containers. Shallow containers should be used instead of deep containers;
- maximize differential – the greater the difference in temperatures between the product and its surroundings, the faster it will cool; and
- air flow from a fan about 10cm from the food will increase heat transfer by a factor of 3 (food should be covered).

Although there is a potential hazard if food is cooled too slowly, the risk may be smaller than that from post-cooking contamination, e.g. slicing with a dirty knife.

Blast chillers

This is equipment designed specifically for the rapid chilling of food. Usually, chilled air at 2°C to 7°C is circulated in a cabinet around the product. Some blast chillers use the vapour from liquid nitrogen and solid carbon dioxide. Some equipment can be set to hold foods after chilling, acting as a normal refrigerator. Alternatively, if suitable blast-chilling equipment is not

Food must be cooled quickly

available, hot food can be cooled rapidly in an otherwise empty freezer and taken out when safe temperatures have been reached, for storage in a refrigerator.

For cooling liquids, ice cream freezers can be used and, for very large quantities, vacuum chillers are available.

Distribution of high-risk food

Vehicles used for the distribution of high-risk food must always be insulated and preferably refrigerated, even for short journeys. Insulation of the roof and floor is just as important as the insulation of the walls. Properly located thermometers should be fitted to all vehicles.

Vehicles must be maintained in a clean and tidy condition. Raw food should never be transported with high-risk food unless they are completely segregated to avoid any risk of contamination. Stacking of vehicles should facilitate sufficient air circulation around the food.

Deliveries of high-risk food

The temperature of food should be checked on arrival. Food requiring refrigerated storage should be rejected if above 8°C and frozen food rejected if above -12°C. Deliveries must be placed in cold storage as quickly as possible to avoid temperatures exceeding the above rejection temperatures.

THE STORAGE OF FROZEN FOOD

At temperatures of around -40°C, most frozen food should keep for several years without noticeable deterioration. However, most domestic and retail freezers operate at -18°C. At this temperature a gradual loss of flavour and a toughening of texture occurs. Above -10°C spoilage organisms commence growth and, together with enzymes, can cause serious problems including souring, putrefaction and rancidity.

All frozen food should be coded to enable the recall of suspect batches which have escaped manufacturing controls.

Storage of frozen food at retail premises

To ensure that customers receive the highest quality of frozen food, managers must:

♦ only use reputable suppliers;
♦ reject deliveries above -12°C or which show signs of thawing or having been refrozen, for example, packs of peas which have welded solid;
♦ not allow frozen food to remain at ambient temperatures for longer than 15 minutes. Food will, of necessity, be at ambient temperatures during unloading of deliveries and stocking display units from back-up stores;
♦ not use display freezers for freezing fresh food, as they are only capable of maintaining the temperature of food which is already frozen;
♦ ensure that display units are not filled above the load-line;
♦ carry out regular inspections of freezers and check temperatures at least daily but preferably more frequently. Electronic probe thermometers should be used to ensure the accuracy of the indicating thermometers which should be fitted to all units in an easily readable position;
♦ ensure that back-up stores are fitted with strip-curtains or air blowers and the doors are opened as little as possible to avoid unacceptable fluctuations of temperature. Ice build-up on the walls or floor of units must not be allowed;
♦ implement effective systems of stock control and stock rotation. It is advisable to code food on delivery to assist rotation; and
♦ ensure that food is not mishandled. Damage to packaging may result in loss of product, contamination and freezer burn. For similar reasons packaging, designed to protect frozen food, must not be removed.

Storage times

All food should be used within the time recommended by the manufacturer.

However, a general guide for food kept at -18°C is:

♦ vegetables, fruit and most meat up to 12 months; and
♦ pork sausages, offal, fatty fish, butter and soft cheeses up to 6 months.

Salad vegetables, non-homogenized milk, single cream, eggs and bananas should not be frozen. Cream can be whipped and stabilized to overcome the separation in desserts. The star marking system is used to indicate the temperature and storage times of food in a frozen storage compartment.

Freezing and refreezing

Freezing of food will not improve its quality. The slow freezing of food in domestic freezers results in the formation of large ice crystals which rupture cells, leading to a slight deterioration in quality, due to changes in the composition of proteins in the presence of enzymes. This deterioration is much more noticeable if food is thawed and refrozen, apart from the obvious dangers if the thawed food is maintained above 10°C for a considerable time. Large ice crystals are particularly noticeable in ice cream which has been refrozen. However, food which has been frozen, thawed and thoroughly cooked may be refrozen quite safely, although flavour and texture will be altered and nutritional value lowered.

Effect of fluctuating temperatures

Clear plastic packaging of food may act as a greenhouse and the radiant heat from fluorescent tubes and air conditioning may increase the temperature of frozen food significantly. Fluctuations from 3°C to 18°C have been observed with the lower temperatures only being achieved during the night when heat sources have been switched off.

Freezer breakdown

If the freezer breaks down or food becomes thawed, for example, due to a power failure, the food may occasionally be treated as fresh. In certain circumstances the food may be cooked and refrozen. If the food has a solid core of ice it may be safe to refreeze without cooking. If in doubt advice should be obtained from the local Environmental Health Department.

In the event of breakdown, the lid of the freezer should be left closed and the unit covered in newspapers and blankets until repaired. Food may remain frozen for at least two days in a well-stocked, well-insulated freezer.

Thawing of frozen food

Many foods taken from the freezer can be cooked immediately but poultry, joints of meat and other large items must be completely thawed before cooking. The manufacturer's instructions should always be followed. If food is not completely thawed, ice is likely to be present at the centre and the heat from subsequent cooking will be used to melt the ice and not to raise the internal temperature above that required to destroy pathogens.

Thawing at room temperatures (25°C to 30°C) may result in the multiplication of bacteria on the warm surface of food, whilst the centre remains frozen. Thawing in a small refrigerator, operating at 1°C to 4°C, can be even more hazardous, if the food does not thaw completely. A 10kg turkey will take several days to thaw and the surfaces of the refrigerator, and high-risk food, may become contaminated with thawed liquid containing pathogenic bacteria. Thawing of frozen poultry is best carried out in a thawing cabinet or at 10°C to 15°C in a well-ventilated area entirely separate from other foods or in cold running water. Thawed food which is stored under refrigeration, as it is not required for immediate use, should be marked with a new date code.

Rules for handling frozen poultry

♦ segregate from high-risk food;
♦ thaw completely in a cool room at less than 15°C or in a thawing cabinet. Clean, cold running water is preferable to thawing in warm kitchen temperatures or in refrigerators with limited space. Poultry will be ready for cooking when the body is pliable, the legs are flexible and the body cavity is free from ice crystals;
♦ remove giblets;
♦ once thawed keep in the refrigerator and cook within 24 hours;
♦ cook thoroughly and cook the stuffing separately;
♦ all utensils and surfaces used for the preparation of raw meat and poultry should be thoroughly cleaned and disinfected before being used for high-risk food. It is preferable to use separate work surfaces;
♦ eat straight after cooking or maintain above 63°C or, if the bird is carved cold, cool it quickly and store in the refrigerator. As with all meats refrigerated storage is essential within 1.5 hours; and
♦ avoid handling the cooked bird unnecessarily.

COOK-CHILL

Cook-chill is the name given to a catering system in which food is thoroughly cooked and then chilled rapidly in a blast chiller to a temperature of 3°C or below within 1.5 hours. The food is stored between 0°C and 3°C until required for reheating. The food is usually produced in a central production unit (CPU) and transported to satellite kitchens for regeneration (reheating).

There are usually nine stages in a cook-chill system:

♦ bulk storage;
♦ preparation;
♦ blast chilling;
♦ distribution at or below 3°C;
♦ serving.
♦ cooking to at least 75°C;
♦ portioning, packaging and labelling;
♦ storage at or below 3°C;
♦ regeneration to at least 75°C; and

The following benefits are claimed for the cook-chill system:

♦ cost-effectiveness – fewer staff, reduction in overtime, shift and weekend working, central purchasing, better utilisation of equipment and reduced floor space;

♦ better staff conditions and less work in unsociable hours. Staff turnover is usually reduced;

♦ flexibility – orders for meals can be accepted at much shorter notice;

♦ more accurate portioning and less wastage; and

♦ improved consistency, quality and palatability compared with meals kept hot, above 63°C, for long periods. Complaints of dried-up and overcooked food should not occur.

Cook-chill demands considerable management and supervisory skills and considerable forward planning. In order to ensure the safety of cook-chill the following rules should be observed:

♦ good quality raw materials;

♦ good design to ensure continuous workflow from raw material to finished product. Cross-contamination must be avoided;

♦ controlled thawing of frozen ingredients;

♦ the implementation of HACCP or systems based on the principles of HACCP;

♦ high standards of hygiene, especially personal hygiene;

♦ food cooked, without delay, to a minimum temperature of 75°C;

♦ food portioned and chilled to below 3°C within two hours of cooking;

♦ hygienic food containers utilized and date marked;

♦ the refrigerated store should maintain food at between 0°C to 3°C and should be fitted with indicating thermometers and alarms;

♦ the maximum life of the food is five days, including the day of production and the day of consumption;

♦ should the temperature of the food exceed 5°C it should be eaten within 12 hours, if the temperature exceeds 10°C during storage or distribution it should be destroyed;

♦ refrigerated vehicles are preferred for distribution but pre-chilled insulated containers may suffice for short journeys;

♦ food must be regenerated as soon as possible when removed from storage; and

♦ a centre temperature of at least 75°C should be achieved using effective heating units. Service should commence within 15 minutes and temperatures should not drop below 63°C.

COOK-FREEZE

The first four stages of cook-freeze are the same as cook-chill, namely bulk storage, preparation, cooking and portioning, packaging and labelling. The fifth stage is blast-freezing. Pre-cooked, lidded packs are loaded onto trolleys which are wheeled into tunnel-type blast-freezers which reduce the temperature to -20°C in less than 90 minutes. Rapid freezing is essential to avoid the formation of large ice crystals which result in poor texture and loss of nutritional value on regeneration. The frozen containers are kept at -20°C and may be stored for up to 12 months.

The exact number of meals required can be removed from storage on demand and regenerated to a temperature of at least 75°C in serving kitchens using, for example, forced-air convection ovens.

REHEATING AND HOT HOLDING

Reheating food presents a major potential hazard in that bacterial growth may occur during the heating-up phase and during any subsequent storage, if sufficiently high temperatures are not reached and then maintained. Generally, food should be reheated as rapidly as possible, to a temperature of at least 75°C (82°C in Scotland) and then held at 63°C or above, until served.

Thorough reheating of food is essential

To ensure adequate reheating, bulk should be minimized and, to ensure rapid penetration of heat, 'surround' systems, such as specialist regeneration ovens may be used. Microwave ovens are a successful and efficient means of reheating, providing the food has a high water content. However, domestic models should not be used in commercial practice. Commercial convector-microwave ovens are particularly useful.

Liquid products, such as soups, should be brought to the boil and kept boiling for several minutes before use, to ensure destruction of toxins. The hot liquids may then need cooling before they can be served, to avoid scalding.

Hot holding

A variety of equipment is available for keeping food hot, pending service. Liquids, semi-liquids and particulate products, such as vegetables and ready-to-eat portions of meat, may be kept in bains marie. These should always be brought up to operating temperature before use, and should not on any account be used for reheating foods. In water baths, checks should be made to ensure that the water levels are kept high. Topping-up should be with hot or boiling water. Container sizes should be matched to the water depth, limiting the amount of product which is above the water level.

Hot cupboards and hot plates may be used for storing reheated products. The latter are particularly valuable when used in conjunction with heating light arrays, but care should be taken to ensure that foods are kept fully in the lit areas, which corresponds with the areas exposed to the radiant heat.

On no account should any food which has been cooled and then reheated be then cooled again for further use. If a food which has been through the full cycle of cooking, cooling and reheating, with or without subsequent hot-holding, remains unsold, it should be disposed of.

Key points

♦ Raw food is likely to be contaminated with pathogenic microorganisms and should be considered as potentially hazardous.

♦ Raw food should always be stored and prepared separate from ready-to-eat food.

♦ Vacuum packs should be stored under refrigeration.

♦ Satisfactory stock rotation is essential to avoid spoilage and waste food. Food must not be sold after its 'use-by' date.

♦ Refrigerators should usually operate between 1°C and 4°C.

♦ A core temperature of 75°C is recommended for cooking most foods.

♦ Hot food must be cooled rapidly. Although joints may take up to eight hours to cool to 3°C.

♦ Freezers should operate at -18°C.

♦ Frozen poultry and large joints must be completely thawed prior to cooking.

♦ If food is stored hot it should be kept above 63°C.

♦ If food is reheated a temperature of at least 75°C, and 82°C in Scotland, is required.

♦ Dry goods stores should be dry, cool and pest free.

7 Food spoilage and preservation

Immediately vegetables and fruit are harvested, fish are taken from the sea or animals are slaughtered, they start decomposing (spoiling). There are two ways in which this can occur:

♦ by the action of natural chemicals (enzymes) already in the food. These are known as autolytic (or self-splitting) enzymes; and

♦ by the action of enzymes from bacteria, moulds and yeasts. These are released by the organisms to break down the food so that it can be absorbed by them.

Spoilage usually starts with aerobes and facultative anaerobes. Then, as the oxygen is used up, obligate anaerobes take over. Moulds and yeasts tend to cause spoilage when the conditions do not favour bacterial growth. Signs of spoilage include discolouration, off odours and taste, slime, rancidity, gas production and changes to the taste and texture. Cans and packs may 'blow'.

How fast food spoils depends on the condition of the food, the pH, water availability, temperature, oxygen, the presence of inhibitory substances (preservatives) and the type and number of spoilage organisms present.

Insects or vermin, and parasites, can also spoil food. So can some chemicals which, even at very low levels, can cause unacceptable taint. Contamination, and the action of oxygen (oxidation), can cause deterioration. Even excessive cold can cause damage by extracting water from the food, a fault known as freezer burn.

Foods which are most prone to spoilage are known as 'perishable'. These include meat, poultry, fish, dairy products, fruit and vegetables. Foods, such as sugar, flour and dried fruit, are unlikely to be affected by spoilage unless they are handled badly, for example, by storing under damp conditions. These are often described as stable or 'non-perishable'.

The presence of mould usually results in food having a musty odour and flavour and, although usually considered harmless, increasing concern is being expressed about fungal toxins known as mycotoxins.

The acidity of fruit ensures that most primary spoilage is caused by moulds and yeasts which are able to multiply at higher acidity than bacteria. Thus, vegetables stored in vinegar, such as beetroot, may be attacked by yeasts. Yeast spoilage of food can often be detected by the alcoholic taste and smell and the presence of bubbles in liquid. Moulds are responsible for most of the spoilage of baked products, especially bread and pies. As mould spores are destroyed by normal cooking temperatures, the spoilage usually arises from airborne spores and contact with contaminated surfaces after cooking.

Rope in bread and other bakery products is caused by a spore-forming bacterium in the flour. Affected bread becomes yellow or brown and develops a fruity, sickly smell and a soft sticky texture. Chemical preservatives are used to prevent rope.

Staleness of bread usually develops with prolonged holding, due to physical changes in the carbohydrates. Refrigeration increases the rate of staling, however, staling does not occur during frozen storage at -18°C.

Rancidity

Rancidity is the term used to describe the breakdown of fats or fatty substances. It occurs when the fats are broken down into free fatty acids by naturally occurring enzymes, known as lipases. These can also be produced by microorganisms. Heating may destroy lipase-producing bacteria but not any lipase already formed and rancidity may still occur.

Rancidity may also occur as a result of the interaction between fats and oxygen, often in the presence of copper or iron contamination. The prolonged cold storage of fatty fish, bacon and pork results in rancidity unless vacuum packed.

FOOD PRESERVATION

Preservation is the treatment of food to prevent or delay spoilage and inhibit growth of pathogenic organisms which would render the food unfit. Preservation may involve:

♦ the use of low temperatures or high temperatures;
♦ moisture reduction;
♦ the use of chemicals;
♦ acid fermentation;
♦ controlled atmospheres and the restriction of oxygen(vacuum packing);
♦ smoking; and
♦ irradiation.

Food preservation: smoking

Food preservation by the use of low temperatures

This form of preservation is primarily to prevent spoilage by microorganisms, the enzyme-producing activity of which is slowed down or arrested by low temperatures. Temperatures used may be:

♦ above freezing (refrigerator);   ♦ below freezing (freezer); and
♦ at freezing (commercially used with chilled beef).

Temperatures above freezing

Refrigerators, operating at between 1°C and 4°C, are suitable for the short-term storage of most perishable foods. Most common pathogenic organisms stop growing below 5°C. Some can continue to grow down to about -2°C, although the growth rate is slow. Certain spoilage bacteria, and moulds, can also cause spoilage at refrigeration temperatures.

Temperatures below freezing

Freezing reduces the moisture available for bacterial growth and significantly reduces enzyme activity. It also destroys some bacteria, including pathogens, and a gradual reduction occurs during storage. Some parasites can also be destroyed by freezing. However, bacterial spores and toxins are generally unaffected.

Moulds and yeasts are more likely to grow on frozen food than bacteria as they are better able to withstand the reduced water availability and the low temperatures. In practice very few organisms grow below -10°C. On thawing, however, surviving bacteria can grow rapidly, compensating for those destroyed, especially if food reaches temperatures of 20°C or higher.

Before vegetables are frozen they must be blanched by dipping in hot water for a short period, approximately one minute. Blanching destroys enzymes which produce off-odours and flavours, and reduces the bacterial load. It also fixes colour, removes trapped air and softens some vegetables, which helps packing. Overblanching will result in excessive loss of vitamin C.

During the freezing process, ice crystals are formed. The slower the rate of freezing, the larger are the ice crystals formed, which can damage certain foods. To avoid this, quick freezing techniques are used.

Most foods will keep for prolonged periods in a freezer, although a recommended shelf-life is given because of loss of texture, flavour, tenderness, colour and overall nutritional quality.

Foods must be properly wrapped to avoid loss of moisture from the surface, i.e. freezer burn. The oxidation of food is slower at -18°C and this also assists in preservation. However, vacuum packing is essential to extend the shelf-life of frozen food susceptible to oxidative rancidity, for example, bacon.

Freezing systems

There are several commercial systems used to freeze food. Air-blast freezing is the commonest. It uses static tunnels where trolleys of boxed product, such as beef and cakes, are passed through. Solid continuous-belt freezers are used for fish fillets, patties and pizzas. Air circulates around the food at temperatures of -30°C to -40°C. Plate freezing is used for food packed in flat cartons, for example, fish blocks and ready-meals. The cartons are placed between narrow metal shelves in which a very cold refrigerant circulates, so ensuring freezing. For products like peas, a process called fluidized-bed freezing can be used. The food is moved along a tunnel on a perforated tray, borne along by a cushion of freezing air forced up from below. Each item is individually quick frozen. In cryogenic freezing, food is sprayed with, or dipped into, a refrigerant such as liquid nitrogen. This is very quick, although more expensive than conventional techniques.

FOOD PRESERVATION BY THE USE OF HIGH TEMPERATURES

Heat treatment is used to destroy enzymes and spoilage and pathogenic organisms and so preserve food. However, heat-resistant bacteria, some toxins and spores may survive. Furthermore, unless very high time/temperature combinations are used, some normal bacteria will survive. The number depends on the initial loading, the strain of organism, the acidity and the presence of protective substances such as proteins and fats.

To prevent recontamination of food after processing, suitable packaging is used, for example, bottles or cans, which can also prevent the multiplication of surviving bacteria. Alternatively, or additionally, products are kept refrigerated.

Pasteurization

Pasteurization involves heating food at a relatively low temperature for a short time, sufficient to kill target pathogens while keeping changes to the food at a minimum. A slight reduction in vitamins and nutritional value will occur. The process is commonly applied to milk, which may be heated at 72°C for 15 seconds and immediately cooled to below 10°C. The actual time and temperature combination chosen depends on the type of food and must be sufficient to destroy vegetative pathogens and most spoilage organisms, although *Lacto bacillus* can survive. Liquid egg can be pasteurized at 64.4°C for at least 2.5 minutes. Following pasteurization, the treated egg must satisfy the alpha-amylase test. Toxins and spores generally survive pasteurization.

Sterilization

Sterilization involves the destruction of all microorganisms. This is sometimes difficult to achieve, so processes are often designed only to destroy viable organisms, i.e. not spores. In this case food is considered 'commercially sterile'. This means that organisms surviving treatment will be of no significance under normal methods of storage. Low-acid canned food is given such a treatment. Sterilization temperatures normally exceed 100°C and are usually achieved by means of steam under pressure.

The main advantage of sterilization is prolonged shelf-life. The main objections are a lowering of nutritional value, including loss of vitamins, and a marked difference in texture and flavour.

Ultra heat treatment (UHT)

The ultra heat treatment of milk is a technique used to extend its shelf-life without the changes caused by sterilization. Nutritional value is similar to that of pasteurized milk. Milk is heated to a temperature of not less than 135°C for one second before filling aseptically into sterile containers. This reduces the amount of caramelization and also enhances keeping quality. UHT milk will keep for several months without refrigeration.

Cooking

Cooking is a form of preservation but is essentially used to make food more palatable and safe for immediate consumption. Temperatures achieved during cooking are usually sufficient to ensure an effective reduction, or the elimination, of vegetative pathogens, although some preformed toxins and spores may be unaffected. In some cases, cooking activates spores and a significant multiplication of vegetative bacteria may occur during subsequent cooling. Internal temperatures of at least 75°C should be achieved to ensure bacteriological safety, although heating food to a lower temperature for longer periods of time may be equally as effective.

Cooked products, such as vegetables, will deteriorate more rapidly than raw products, and other methods of preservation must be used to prolong shelf-life if stored, for example, refrigeration, freezing or canning.

Canning

Unlike most other forms of preservation the food inside the can remains an ideal medium for bacterial growth. It is therefore imperative that:

◆ the heat process destroys all anaerobic pathogenic and spoilage microorganisms;

◆ the closure of the can precludes the entry of microorganisms; and

◆ the post-process handling of the can prevents damage and subsequent contamination.

The most heat-resistant pathogenic organism is *Clostridium botulinum* and this bacterium will not grow below a pH of 4.5. Consequently, when determining the heat process, regard must be had for the pH of the can contents. All foods with a pH of less than 4.5 are known as acid foods and those with a pH of more than 4.5 are termed low-acid foods.

Most fruits have a pH of less than 4.5 and consequently only receive a relatively low pasteurizing heat process. Vegetables and meats have pHs much higher than 4.5 and they are given a process known as a 'botulinum cook' to render them commercially sterile.

Before canned food is heat processed it is normally prepared in some way. The actual process of preparation will vary depending on the food type but the following flow chart shows the usual processes involved.

A schematic diagram of canning operations

RAW MATERIALS

Fruit & Vegetables – washing, peeling, grading and blanching.
Meats – cleaning, boning, cutting and curing.
Fish – washing, gutting and brining.
Milk products – filtering, standardizing and homogenizing.

INSPECTION
(including metal detection and magnets)

Cans inverted and washed

FILLING (normally hot)

Mixed packs
Brine/syrup

SEALING TO CREATE VACUUM & CODING

Double seam to hermetically seal the can

PROCESSING: THE 'BOTULINUM COOK'

Using retorts, hydrostatic pressure vessels or horizontal cookers

COOLING

Chlorinated water

DRYING

LABELLING & SHRINK WRAPPING

STORAGE & DISTRIBUTION

The minimum safe thermal process for a low-acid canned food is one which would reduce the chance of survival of one spore of *Clostridium botulinum* to less than one in 10^{12}. This is achieved by ensuring the core of the food reaches a minimum of 121°C for three minutes, or an equivalent time and temperature combination. After the heating process the cans must be cooled with chlorinated water. The greatest care must be taken after heat treatment, especially whilst the can is still warm and wet, and before the sealing compound has hardened. Bacteria are capable of being sucked into visually satisfactory cans through microscopic holes in the seams. If these bacteria are spoilage or pathogenic organisms, problems will occur. Warm, wet cans must not be handled.

Pasteurized canned foods

As discussed earlier, most low-acid canned foods are processed to a minimum standard of the 'botulinum cook'. However, some foods if fully processed would be inedible. One example of this is canned cured ham. This product only receives a pasteurization process (a centre temperature of about 70°C). This means that chilled storage is essential to ensure its safety.

MOISTURE REDUCTION AS A MEANS OF PRESERVATION

All microorganisms need moisture to multiply. Dehydration reduces the amount of available water and thus prevents growth. However, some bacterial spores will germinate on the reconstitution of the dried product. Although yeasts and moulds usually grow at lower moisture levels than do bacteria, mould spoilage is also prevented, as is enzyme activity. Provided dried foods are stored in suitable air-tight packs, and kept dry, they will keep for a considerable period of time.

Sun drying was the earliest method of dehydration and is still practised in hot climates, for example, for drying currants, raisins and figs. Artificial drying is quicker and normally more effective than natural means. Unfortunately, food undergoes irreversible changes to the tissue structure during drying, which affects both texture and flavour.

Artificial drying techniques include the use of hot air, for example in tunnel drying, fluidized-bed drying, roller drying and spray drying. Changes in protein structure and flavour can be reduced by using warm air, as in accelerated freeze drying. The choice of technique often depends on the type of foodstuff and the degree of dehydration required. Blanching of vegetables must be carried out before drying to obviate enzyme activity during storage.

In spray drying, a solution, paste or slurry is dispersed as small droplets into a stream of hot air. The small droplets result in a rapid loss of moisture and a large proportion of the colour, flavour and nutritive value of the food is maintained. However, because the evaporative cooling effect keeps the temperature of the droplets low, a pasteurization process is usually required prior to spray drying.

In roller drying, the food is turned into a paste which is dried on a heated drum and scraped off. Generally, product quality is inferior to spray-dried product. For fruits and vegetables, a tunnel drier, 10 to 15 metres long, is used. Trays of product are passed through it while hot air is blown across the trays. This continuous process leads to a gradual loss of moisture. Total removal of moisture may not be necessary. The remaining water forms a strong solution with salts and soluble proteins. This water remaining is not available to microorganisms.

Accelerated freeze drying

Food is frozen quickly and then lightly heated under vacuum. Ice in the food is then extracted as water vapour, a process known as sublimation. The processes minimizes the effects of drying and the product reconstitutes better.

CHEMICAL METHODS OF PRESERVATION

A wide range of chemical additives is available for food preservation and may be used to prevent microbial spoilage, chemical deterioration and mould growth. As high concentration of some chemicals, such as sulphur dioxide and sodium nitrate are poisonous, the use of additives is strictly controlled by legislation and maximum permitted levels are usually specified. Preservatives used include:

(1) Salt: Salt reduces the water available (a_W) to bacteria. Its effectiveness depends on the concentration, contamination levels, pH, temperature, protein content and the presence of other inhibitory substances. In use, it may be rubbed into meat or, as brine, injected into the muscular tissue. It can also be an ingredient in the manufacture of sausages and used to preserve fish.

Some microorganisms are salt-tolerant but this tolerance is usually decreased by lowering the temperature or the pH. Moulds are less affected by salt. Staphylococci will grow in relatively high salt concentrations and are often associated with food poisoning from semi-preserved salted meats.

In preservation the use of salt, with the addition of other chemicals such as sodium nitrate, is termed curing. Its use for flavour or colouring is termed brining.

(2) Nitrates and nitrites: Sodium nitrate and sodium nitrite salts are used in curing meat. They help retain colour and reduce spoilage. They are also essential in such products as pasteurized ham to stop the production of botulinum toxin, by preventing the germination of spores.

Traditionally, salt and nitrate solutions were injected into meat, which was then immersed in brine to enable salt tolerant bacteria to convert nitrate to nitrite. Currently, nitrites tend to be used direct as they are much more effective than nitrates.

The effectiveness of curing salts depends on various factors, including the pH of the meat, the number and types of microorganisms present and the curing temperature.

(3) Sugar: Sugar acts in a similar manner to salt but concentrations need to be about six times higher. It is commonly used for jam and other preserves, candied fruit and condensed milk. Certain types of cake have increased shelf-life due to the effect of sugar.

(4) Sulphur dioxide/sulphite: Sulphur dioxide may be used in gaseous or liquid form or as a salt. It is an antioxidant and also inhibits growth of bacteria and moulds. It is used in some foods to prevent enzymatic browning. Sulphur dioxide is also used in wine, beers, fruit juice and comminuted meat products, including sausages, where it is allowed up to 450µg/g. Apart from reducing the growth of spoilage organisms, sulphur dioxide also limits the growth of salmonellae.

(5) Pickling/acidification: This process involves using an acid such as acetic acid, i.e. vinegar, to acidify the food to create an environment in which microorganisms will not multiply. The acidification process is controlled so that the pH of each part of the product drops below 4.5.

(6) Sodium and calcium propionate: Propionates are active in low-acid foods and very useful to prohibit mould growth. They are used in bread, cakes, cheese, grain and jellies.

(7) Antibiotics: These chemicals have a preservative role in addition to their normal function. Their use is strictly controlled by regulations to avoid the build-up of resistance by pathogenic organisms. An example of an antibiotic used for preservation is nisin, added to some cheeses and canned foods. Nisin is heat-resistant but is destroyed during digestion and should not cause problems of pathogen drug resistance.

FERMENTATION

Fermented foods are produced by the activities of bacteria, yeasts or moulds and include cheese, yoghurt, salami, sauerkraut, pepperoni, bread and soy sauce. The fermentation process involves the use of starter cultures, for example lactic acid bacteria added to milk to produce yoghurt. Lactic acid bacteria ferment carbohydrates such as glucose to produce lactic acid which lowers the pH to preserve the food. Yeast fermentation produces carbon dioxide and ethanol.

CONTROLLED ATMOSPHERES

One of the simplest food preservation methods is to change the atmosphere around the food. This is termed modified atmosphere packaging (MAP). The proportion of the gases normally present around a product is modified to contain, for example, lower levels of oxygen and higher levels of nitrogen and carbon dioxide. This slows down the growth of many spoilage organisms and extends shelf-life. MAP should also be combined with correct chilled temperature control in order to guarantee the control of microbial proliferation.

The restriction of oxygen

The development of oxidative rancidity and the growth of strict aerobes such as moulds can be prevented by vacuum packing, although sufficient oxygen normally remains in vacuum packs of meat to facilitate the growth of some aerobes. Complete removal of oxygen allows the growth of anaerobes such as *Clostridium perfringens*.

Vacuum packs of cooked meat must be stored under refrigeration to achieve a reasonable shelf-life.

SMOKING

Smoking is applied primarily to meat and fish, after brining or pickling, by suspending the food over smouldering hardwoods such as oak and ash. It is often used only to enhance flavour. Smoking also has some dehydrating effect and there may be some preserving action due to the presence of bactericidal chemicals in smoke. Most non-sporing bacteria will be destroyed but moulds and *Cl. botulinum* type E may survive, especially in low salt concentrations. Smoked products should, therefore, be refrigerated at 3°C or below.

Cold smoked food should be treated as raw and hot smoked food should be considered as high-risk food.

Another way of adding a smoke flavour to the food is to spray a liquid, produced by trapping smoke in water, on to the food. The preserving effect is limited and the food is not dehydrated.

FOOD IRRADIATION

This form of preservation involves subjecting the food to a dose of ionizing radiation. It is an effective and safe method of extending shelf-life. It destroys parasites, insects including eggs, bacteria, moulds and yeasts. However, microbial spores and toxins remain unaffected at the levels used. Foods most commonly irradiated outside the UK include chicken, fish, prawns, onions, potatoes, spices and strawberries. Irradiation may be used as part of a continuous or batch process.(In the UK only spices may be subject to irradiation)

Preservation using irradiation has the same limitations as many other preservation techniques. Vitamins may be destroyed and enzymes are not deactivated. Other disadvantages include the encouragement of oxidative rancidity in fatty foods, the possible production of free radicals in food that stimulate a range of chemical reactions, and the softening of some fruit.

Key points
♦ Spoilage of food commences when vegetables and fruit are harvested, animals are slaughtered and fish are removed from the sea.
♦ Spoilage occurs because of the action of enzymes, bacteria, moulds, yeasts and pests.
♦ Refrigeration of perishable foods slows down spoilage.
♦ Food preservation prevents or delays spoilage and inhibits the growth of pathogenic organisms.
♦ Preservation may involve: the use of low or high temperatures; dehydration; chemicals; controlled atmospheres and physical methods.
♦ Foods should be cooked to a centre temperature of at least 75°C.

8 The design and construction of food premises and equipment

A well-planned layout and the use of satisfactory building materials are essential to achieve high standards of hygiene. The size of the premises must facilitate efficient operation and the site must be large enough to accommodate possible future expansion.

Selection of a suitable site

The site must have sufficient services, i.e. electricity and gas, water supply and effluent disposal, and be accessible for delivery and waste disposal. It should not be liable to flooding or unacceptable contamination from chemicals, dust, odour or pests. Potential for noise emissions should be considered if there are nearby residential premises.

General principles of design

To achieve a satisfactory design, the following principles should be considered:

- ◆ clean and dirty processes must be separated to minimize the risk of contamination. Where possible:
  - a. work areas should be segregated into pre-cook and post-cook; and
  - b. a separate area should be provided for de-boxing and unwrapping raw materials.
- ◆ workflow should be continuous and progress in a uniform direction from raw material to finished product. Distances travelled by raw materials, utensils, food containers, waste food, packaging materials and staff should be minimized;
- ◆ facilities for personal hygiene and disinfection of small items of equipment should relate to working areas and process risks;
- ◆ where appropriate, suitable facilities must be provided for temperature, humidity and other controls;
- ◆ the premises must be capable of being thoroughly cleaned and, if necessary, disinfected at the end of production;
- ◆ insects, rodents and birds must be denied access and harbourage;
- ◆ yard surfaces and roads within the boundary of the premises must have a suitable impervious surface with adequate drainage, and provision made for refuse storage; and
- ◆ suitable provision must be made for staff welfare, including cloakroom and, if necessary, canteen and first aid facilities.

THE CONSTRUCTION OF FOOD PREMISES

It is essential that the correct materials are chosen for all internal finishes and that they are properly fixed or applied. Materials should be non-toxic, durable and easy to maintain and clean.

Ceilings

Suspended ceilings are advantageous as horizontal pipework and services can be concealed in the ceiling void. They are normally constructed from a metal lattice incorporating cleansable panels. Aluminium backed and faced fibre-board has proved successful in many food factories. Flush-fitting ventilation grilles and lighting will often be provided.

Solid ceilings should be well insulated, smooth, fire resistant, light-coloured, and coved at wall joints. Finishes should be washable. A non-flaking emulsion may be suitable. Special attention must be paid to ceiling finishes above heat and/or steam-producing appliances such as ovens, sinks and retorts. Canopies and separate extraction units may be fitted in these areas.

Ceiling height will vary depending on the type of operations being carried out but should be high enough to provide satisfactory working conditions and allow the installation of equipment.

Walls

Smooth, impervious, non-flaking, durable, light-coloured wall surfaces are required which must be capable of being thoroughly cleaned and, if necessary, disinfected. Internal solid walls are preferable to those with cavities.

When constructing factories, it can be advantageous to use modular buildings, of standard dimensions, with the actual production areas built inside the external structure, leaving clear walkways outside these areas, but within the overall structure. The 'building within the building' can be fabricated from modular panels of the type used for cold-store construction.

Wall surfaces in use include resin-bonded fibre glass, ceramic-faced blocks, plastic panelling, epoxy resin, glazed tiles with water-resistant grouting and rubberized paint on hard plaster or sealed brickwork. Some paints incorporate a fungicidal additive. Galvanized steel, aluminium and stainless steel are also used, and plastic sheeting is popular.

Wall or floor stops are needed to prevent doors damaging wall surfaces, and wall corners should be protected. Crash rails should be used if trolleys are likely to damage wall surfaces, although large, angled fillets to the wall-floor junctions can also prevent trolley impact.

Pipework and ducting should be bracketed at least 150mm from walls to facilitate cleaning. All lagging to pipes must be smooth and impervious. Pipes passing through external walls must be effectively sealed to prevent the ingress of pests.

Windows and doors

Any windows should either be fixed on north-facing walls to reduce glare and solar heat gains, or treated with solar film to counteract heat gain. Cleansable, well-fitting fly-screens must, where necessary, be fitted to opening windows. Windows should be constructed to facilitate cleaning and any internal window sills should be sloped to prevent their use as shelves.

Doors should have smooth, non-absorbent surfaces capable of being thoroughly cleaned. They should be tight-fitting and self-closing. Door handles and finger-plates should be capable of disinfection. Swing doors with kick-plates are preferable to handles. External doorways should, where necessary, be proofed against the entry of insects, and metal kick-plates should be provided to prevent gnawing by rodents. Clear plastic strips can be used to protect openings.

Floors

Regard must be had to initial cost, durability, performance and safety. In food premises, floors should be durable, non-absorbent, anti-slip, without crevices and capable of being effectively cleaned. Where appropriate they must be resistant to acids, grease and salts and should slope sufficiently for liquids to drain to trapped gullies or channels; a slope (or 'fall') of 1 in 60 is the minimum recommended. The junctions between walls and floors should be coved.

Suitable flooring includes epoxy resin, granolithic (concrete incorporating granite chippings), welded anti-slip, vinyl sheet and slip-resistant ceramic or quarry tiles.

Services

These include gas, electricity, water supplies, drainage, lighting and ventilation.

Gas supplies

Supply pipes should always be mounted clear of the floor and never so close to other pipes as to restrict access for cleaning. Flexible connections, to facilitate removal of equipment for cleaning purposes, are recommended.

Electrical supplies

Adequate numbers of power points should be available for all electrical equipment. Cut-out switches for power circuits should be accessible and separate from lighting and ventilation supplies, so that cleaning can take place in safety. Separate cut-out switches should be provided for refrigeration equipment.

Controls should be fixed clear of equipment to avoid becoming dirty or wet during cleaning. Removable electrical components assist cleaning and are advantageous. Surface-mounted electrical wiring should be protected by waterproof conduits. All switches should be flush-fitting and waterproof (especially in production areas).

Water supplies

Cold water supplies for use with food, for cleaning equipment or surfaces or for personal hygiene must be potable (of drinking water standard). They should not be fed via an intermediate tank unless chlorinated; mains supplies are preferable.

Water heating provisions should be able to supply hot water at a target discharge temperature of 60°C, although higher system temperatures may be required to avoid legionnaire's disease. In this case, mixer taps will be needed to avoid scalding. In hard-water areas, provision for softening should be made.

Non-potable water must be conveyed in identifiable systems which have no connection with, nor any possible reflux into, the potable water system. An external water supply should always be available.

Drainage

Premises should have an efficient, smooth-bore drainage system. Drains and sewers should be adequate to remove peak loads quickly without flooding. Sufficient drains should be installed to facilitate effective cleaning of rooms by pressure jet cleaners or other means. Channels or trapped gullies may be used. Grease traps, if fitted, should be large enough to allow adequate time for fat to separate and should be emptied regularly.

The direction of flow should be from clean areas to dirty areas. Toilets should feed into the system after food rooms. Inspection chambers should be placed outside food rooms but if interior location is unavoidable they must be airtight, i.e. triple seal, bolt down. All drainage systems must be provided with sufficient access points to allow rodding in the event of blockages. Petrol interceptors may be required for yard drains.

Drains should be constructed to inhibit the harbourage and movement of vermin. All external rainwater fall-pipes should be fitted with balloon guards to prevent rodent access. Circumference guards should be fitted around all vertical pipes fastened to walls, to prevent rodents climbing up them.

Ventilation

Sufficient ventilation must be provided to produce a satisfactory, safe working environment and to reduce humidities and temperatures which would encourage the rapid multiplication of bacteria. Normally, ambient temperatures should be below 25°C. Natural ventilation often needs supplementing by mechanical ventilation to ensure effective air circulation and adequate air changes. You cannot rely on open windows. Extract ventilation should always flow from a clean to a dirty area. Its function is to prevent excessive heat build-up, condensation, dust, steam, and to remove odours and contaminated air. The source of input air must always be checked to ensure contaminants are not brought in to food rooms.

Steam-producing equipment, such as cookers, boilers and blanchers, should be provided with adequately-sized canopies. Provision of lower heat-emitting equipment such as pressure vessels and microwave ovens, and upgrading insulation on ovens will reduce heat production.

Lighting

Suitable and sufficient lighting must be provided throughout food premises, including store rooms, passageways and stairways, so that employees can identify hazards and carry out tasks correctly.

Artificial lighting is often preferred to natural lighting because of problems of solar heat gain, glare, shadows and flying insects entering open windows. Recommended illumination levels are as follows: 150 lux in storerooms and 500 lux in preparation areas. Fluorescent tubes, fitted with diffusers to prevent glare and product contamination in the event of breakage, are recommended.

Handwashing facilities

Adequate facilities for handwashing and drying should be provided wherever the process demands. In particular, a suitable number of basins or troughs should be sited at the entrance of food rooms to ensure all persons entering wash their hands. Wash-

Inaccessible wash-hand basins

hand basins must be easily accessible, should only be used for washing hands and should not be obstructed. All basins and troughs, preferably made of stainless steel, should be connected to drains by properly trapped waste pipes.

Cleaning and disinfection facilities

Where appropriate, adequate facilities for the cleaning and disinfection of utensils, crockery, cutlery, glasses and equipment should be provided. These facilities will normally be constructed from stainless steel. Twin sinks are preferable to facilitate washing and disinfecting/rinsing. Sinks should be freestanding so that they can be removed easily after unscrewing the lower trap joint, freeing the waste pipe. 'Sterilizing' sinks and units should be capable of operating at 82°C.

Separate sinks must be provided for food preparation and equipment washing if the volume demands it. In small operations the same sink may be used if there is no risk to food safety. Exclusive food sinks may be provided with cold water only.

Sanitary conveniences and washing facilities

All new premises should be provided with adequate staff sanitary accommodation, adequately ventilated and lit. Rooms containing sanitary conveniences must not communicate directly with a room where food is processed, prepared or eaten. Internal wall and floor surfaces should permit wet cleaning.

Foot-operated flushing devices are recommended. Doors to intervening spaces and sanitary accommodation should be self-closing and clearly illustrate the sex of the user. Suitable and sufficient washing facilities must be provided at readily accessible places. In particular, facilities must be provided in the immediate vicinity of every sanitary convenience and supplied with clean hot and cold or warm water, liquid soap and appropriate drying facilities.

Cloakrooms and lockers

Adequate accommodation for outdoor clothing and footwear, not worn by the staff during normal working hours, must be available. Such articles must not be stored in a food room unless in suitable cupboards or lockers provided only for this purpose. Adequate facilities for drying wet clothing should also be provided.

The storage and disposal of waste

Waste disposal systems must be planned, along with other services, when food premises are designed. Refuse collectors should not have to enter food rooms or dining areas.

Waste food should be kept separate from paper and cardboard packaging. In some instances, waste may be stored under refrigeration pending collection, for example, bones in butchers' shops. It is preferable for all waste food to be removed from food premises at least daily and general refuse to be removed at least twice a week.

Dustbins must be kept clean

Suitable facilities must be provided for the storage of waste externally, prior to removal from the establishment. Dustbins or bulk containers are commonly used, although skips and compactors are more appropriate for food factories. Compactors vary from units similar to a large dustbin to refuse-sack compactors and skip rams.

Dustbins should be stored clear of the ground, for example, on tubular steel racks, to facilitate cleaning and removal of spillages. All receptacles should be capable of being cleaned and provided with suitable tight-fitting lids or covers to prevent insects, birds and rodents gaining access. Overflowing bins attract pests.

The refuse area must have a well-drained, impervious surface which is capable of being kept clean. Stand pipes, hoses and, possibly, high-pressure sprayers should be provided for cleaning purposes. Covered areas to protect refuse from the sun and rain are recommended. Satisfactory provision should be made for the disposal of liquid food waste such as oil.

Refuse areas should not be too far from food rooms to discourage their use but they should not be too close to encourage flies to enter the food rooms. They should not be sited next to the main food delivery entrance. Covered ways between refuse areas and food rooms are useful to protect staff against inclement weather.

Perimeter areas

It is recommended that a concrete path, at least 675mm wide, abutting the external walls should be provided around all food buildings. This removes cover for rodents and enables early signs of pests to be discovered, for example, rodent droppings. Paths should be kept clean, free of vegetation and inspected regularly. A smooth band of rendering, around 450mm, at the base of external walls will discourage rodents from climbing. Whenever possible, a perimeter fence should be constructed around food premises to deter unauthorized entry. Areas within perimeter fences must be kept clean and tidy. Rubbish, old equipment and weeds must not be allowed to accumulate or provide harbourage for insects or rodents.

Kitchen design

The layout of a well-designed, commercial kitchen has three main characteristics:
♦   clearly identified and separated flows;

♦ defined accommodation, specific to the purposes allocated; and
♦ economy of space provision (commensurate with good hygiene practice).

The unit should also afford management personnel easy access to the areas under their control and good visibility in the areas which have to be supervised. Space is needed for management function and for equipment such as telephones and computers.

Flows

Four separate flows need to be considered: the food being produced; personnel; containers, utensils and equipment; and waste/refuse. Product flows should be subdivided into high-risk and contaminated (raw food) sections. Clear segregation should be maintained between the two. As far as practicable, flows should be unidirectional, without backtracking or crossover.

Accommodation

Accommodation should be sized according to operational need when at maximum production. Essentially, the working areas, stores, the equipment and its relative spacing should all be determined and laid out to suit the operation.

Areas should be allocated according to environmental compatibility; hot functions with hot, dirty with dirty, wet with wet, dry with dry, defined overall by segregation between high-risk and contaminated food handling.

Equipment required for specific functions should be grouped and accessible, in order to avoid excessive walking and the temptation to take shortcuts. Wash-hand basins should be strategically located to ensure that operatives entering food preparation areas wash their hands.

Size

There should be a minimum of circulation and dead space, commensurate with the efficient functioning of the unit. Size should be neither too small nor too large; there are penalties in the over-provision of space as much as there are problems with too small a provision.

The size of the kitchen can only be determined when its exact purpose and function have been defined. Items to take into consideration include:
♦ the state of raw materials, for example, ready prepared or not;
♦ the extent of the menu and number of sittings;
♦ the equipment used, for example, microwave ovens; and
♦ the amount of dishwashing. Disposable plates, etc. may be used.

THE DESIGN AND CONSTRUCTION OF EQUIPMENT

The hygienic design of equipment is necessary to comply with legislative requirements, avoid product contamination and to facilitate cost-effective cleaning and, if necessary, disinfection.

Poorly designed equipment, which cannot be dismantled, may be uncleanable,

Plan of a well designed kitchen incorporating principles of continuous workflow and segregation of clean and dirty processes (not to scale).*

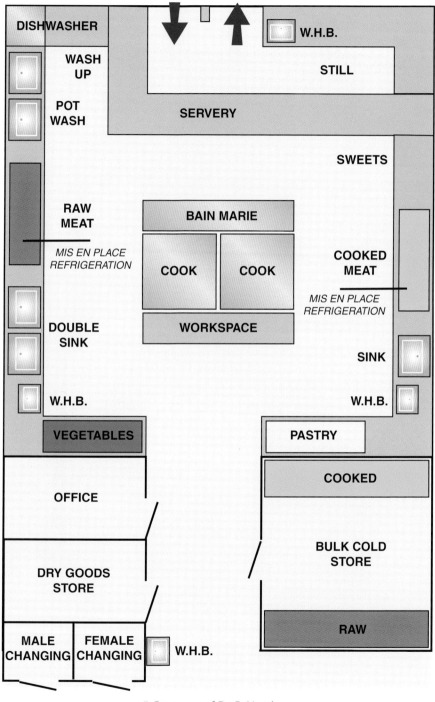

* Courtesy of Dr. R. North

incapable of being chemically disinfected and may result in product contamination by pathogenic bacteria. Even if equipment can be dismantled, unhygienic design may make cleaning and disinfection prohibitively expensive.

The legal requirements

Food safety legislation requires all articles, fittings and equipment with which food comes into contact to:

 ◆ be kept clean;
 ◆ be so constructed, of such materials and maintained in such condition and repair as to minimize risk of contamination; and
 ◆ enable thorough cleaning and, where necessary, disinfection.

Furthermore, equipment must be installed in a way which allows the surrounding area to be cleaned.

The Supply of Machinery (Safety) Regulations, 1992 (as amended in 1994)

The regulations require that new machinery used for preparing and processing foodstuffs carries a CE marking and must be designed and constructed to avoid health risks and in particular:

 ◆ contact materials of foodstuffs must satisfy the conditions set down in the relevant directives. Machinery must be designed and constructed to facilitate cleaning;
 ◆ all surfaces and joints must be smooth, without ridges or crevices which could harbour organic materials;
 ◆ projections, edges and recesses should be minimal. Continuous welding is preferable. Screws and rivets should not be used unless technically unavoidable;
 ◆ contact surfaces must be easily cleaned and disinfected. The design of internal surfaces, angles, etc. must allow thorough cleaning;
 ◆ cleaning residues must drain from equipment surfaces, pipework, etc., there must be no retention in voids;
 ◆ the design should prevent organic accumulations or insect infestation in uncleanable areas, e.g. by the use of castors or alternatively, sealed bases; and
 ◆ lubricants must not come into contact with any product.

In addition, equipment manufacturers must provide accurate information on recommended products and methods of cleaning, disinfecting and rinsing. Equipment should be regularly maintained. Food must be removed prior to maintenance and the area cleaned after maintenance.

Construction materials

Materials in contact with food must be non-toxic, non-tainting and constituents from their surfaces must not migrate into the food or be absorbed by the food in quantities which could endanger health. Materials must have adequate strength over a wide temperature range, a reasonable life, be corrosion and abrasion resistant and be easily cleaned and disinfected. In most meat plants, the use of wood is forbidden except in rooms used for the storage of hygienically packed fresh meat.

The most widely used material is food-grade stainless steel. Some plastics may be suitable, but must be approved for food use. Aluminium should be avoided, as should copper and zinc. Handles of knives, brushes and other equipment should all be made from cleansable materials such as polypropylene or high-density stainless steel.

Surfaces should be non-porous, continuous, non-flaking and free from cracks, crevices and pits. Surfaces will need to retain a satisfactory finish throughout their life including anticipated abuse and normal wear and tear. Joints should be made by welding or continuous bonding to reduce projections, edges and recesses to a minimum.

Equipment exterior

The external surfaces of equipment must avoid ledges and dust traps, for example, round legs are preferred to rectangular. It is important to avoid recessed corners, sharp edges, unfilled seams, uneven surfaces and hollows and projecting bolt heads, threads, screws or rivets that cannot be cleaned. Inaccessible spaces, pockets and crevices where product may accumulate must be absent.

Fixing and siting of equipment

Equipment must be sited so that there is sufficient space to facilitate access to all external and internal surfaces and, where required, to allow for rapid dismantling and reassembly. Machinery may be mounted on coved, raised platforms of concrete to facilitate cleaning. Where necessary, additional space may need to be provided. The bases and lower parts of machines, including motors and gears, may be difficult to clean and consequently collect dust and spillages which make ideal breeding sites for insects. Skirting or cover plates tend to trap dust.

Where practicable, and with due regard for safety, equipment can be mobile to facilitate its removal for cleaning.

Mobile equipment

Drainage

All pipelines, vessels and equipment should be self-draining, not only to enable liquid deriving from foodstuffs to be discharged but also for cleaning and rinsing fluids.

Preparation surfaces

Preparation surfaces should be jointless, durable, impervious, the correct height and provide a firm base on which to work. If materials other than stainless steel are used, for example, food-grade plastic, care should be taken to seal the edges and gaps which may harbour food scraps. They must be able to withstand frequent and repeated cleaning and disinfection without any premature deterioration, pitting or corrosion.

Chopping boards

A variety of non-absorbent materials for chopping boards is now available, including good quality polypropylene. However, some are unsatisfactory. A good board should not split or warp and

Dishwashers should be used for cleaning and disinfecting cutting boards

it is advantageous if it can be passed through a dishwasher.

As yet no ideal replacement has been found for hardwood chopping blocks. However, these should be maintained in good condition and used solely for chopping or sawing raw meat. A common colour-coding system for chopping boards involves using:

RED: for raw meat

GREEN: for salad

BLUE: for fish

YELLOW: for high-risk food

WHITE: for dairy produce

BROWN: for raw vegetables

Contamination

To avoid cross-contamination, it is important that the same equipment is not used for handling raw and high-risk products without being disinfected. To prevent the inadvertent use of equipment for high-risk and raw food the use of different colours and/or shapes is advantageous. Colour coding may be extended from knives and chopping boards to include washing facilities, trolleys, protective clothing, cloths and packaging material.

The cleaning of equipment

All operating instructions and procedures must be clearly communicated to the equipment users and cleaners. The equipment should be capable of being cleaned and, if necessary, disinfected safely, thoroughly and rapidly without the need for skilled fitters and specialized tools. If dismantling is necessary this must be achieved relatively easily, as should reassembly.

Sharp edges are a serious hazard for cleaners. A reluctance to clean equipment because of poor design will result in a lowering of hygienic standards. Hinges should be capable of being taken apart for cleaning. Angle iron is difficult to clean and tubular construction is preferred, open ends to tubular legs must be sealed.

Key points

♦ Good design and the use of satisfactory building materials are essential to achieve high standards of hygiene.

♦ Clean and dirty (raw and high-risk) processes must be separated to minimize risk of contamination.

♦ Workflow must be continuous in a uniform direction from raw material to finished product.

♦ Surfaces and finishes must be non-toxic, non-flaking, durable and easy to maintain and clean.

♦ All food premises must have potable cold water supplies.

♦ Premises must be well lit and ventilated with satisfactory provision for drainage and waste management.

♦ Adequate facilities for handwashing, cleaning and disinfection must be provided.

♦ Equipment must be kept clean and in good condition to minimize risk of contamination.

♦ Colour coding of equipment assists in minimizing the risk of contamination.

Food premises

9 Cleaning and disinfection

In any food business, soiling of both surfaces and equipment is unavoidable. The type and extent of soiling will vary considerably but, whatever the operation, it is essential that residues are not allowed to accumulate to levels which expose food to the risk of contamination.

The benefits of cleaning

Cleaning is an essential and integral part of a profitable food business. In addition to satisfying legal requirements, cleanliness will:

- ensure a pleasant, safe and attractive working environment which will encourage effective working and reduce the risk of accidents to both staff and customers;
- promote a favourable image to the customer and assist in marketing the business;
- remove matter conducive to the growth of microorganisms so facilitating effective disinfection and reducing the risk of food poisoning and spoilage;
- remove materials that would provide food or harbourage for pests and prevent early discovery of infestations;
- reduce the risk of foreign matter contamination and thereby obviate customer complaints;
- prevent damage to, or a reduction in, the efficiency of equipment and services, and reduce maintenance costs.

Problems caused by ineffective or negligent cleaning

Negligent cleaning may achieve a satisfactory physical appearance but can also result in hazardous bacterial contamination, for example, cleaning from raw to high-risk areas. Selection of the appropriate cleaning chemicals often requires expert technical advice as the use of the wrong chemicals, or the right chemicals at the incorrect strength, temperature or contact time, may have serious financial consequences. This not only applies to direct costs relating to product, equipment and premises but also, the cost of effluent treatment. It is also important that all cleaning chemicals are stored separate from food in a locked chemical store. Ineffective or negligent cleaning may result in:

- microbiological hazards, contamination and a poor quality product which may lead to a reduction in shelf-life, customer complaints, loss of reputation, court proceedings, food poisoning, redress from suppliers and loss of sales;
- wastage of food and production re-runs;
- chemical hazards, including taint and other forms of food contamination;
- corrosion and premature replacement of equipment;
- production breakdowns, for example, following the incorrect use of caustic

soda which has removed grease from bearings;
- unacceptable deterioration of floor surfaces and drainage systems; and
- physical contamination hazards from worn and defective cleaning equipment.

Energy in cleaning

Cleaning is defined as 'the systematic application of energy to a surface or substance, with the intention of removing dirt'. Energy is available for cleaning in three distinct forms: kinetic energy: physical – manual labour;

mechanical – machines;

turbulence – liquids

(cleaning in place);

thermal energy: hot water; and

chemical energy: detergents.

Normally, a combination of two or more energy forms is used. Manual labour is the most expensive and chemical energy the most economic, although adequate contact time is also important. The correct energy balance is essential for cost-effective cleaning.

Detergents

Detergents are chemicals, or mixtures of chemicals, made of soap or synthetic substitutes, which are used to remove grease or other soiling and promote cleanliness. They are available as powders, liquids, foams or gels. Detergents should be harmless to operatives and equipment, non-toxic, odourless and tasteless, i.e. non-tainting.

The reduction of surface tension enables detergent solutions to penetrate dirt and grease and lift them from the surface to form a suspension which can then be rinsed away. Cost-effectiveness of the cleaning operation depends on the correct mix of the following:
- choosing the correct chemical;
- applying it at the optimum temperature and concentration;
- allowing it time to function; and
- using it with the correct equipment.

Cleaning equipment

Consistent, high standards of cleanliness will only be achieved if the cleaning tools have been specifically manufactured for the stringent demands of the food industry. Correct choice is essential if operatives are to avoid recontamination of a cleaned surface with dirt or bacteria or, in the case of brushes, the contamination of product with bristles. The quality and cleanliness of tools which touch surfaces in direct contact with food is particularly important.

The use of colour coding for cleaning equipment, for example, handles of brushes, bristles and cloths used in high-risk situations, with different colours being used in raw and high-risk food areas, assists in reducing the risk of cross-contamination and reinforces hygiene training relating to the need to separate raw and high-risk food.

Brushes

Brushes constructed from materials such as high-density polypropylene for stocks with bristles of polyester or rilsan give improved performance and resistance to wear. They are capable of withstanding boiling water and the normal cleaning chemicals used throughout the food industry. Wood and natural bristles must be avoided and worn out brushes must be replaced. As brushes become worn they become less effective, they discolour and bristles are more likely to drop out. Blue coloured bristles are often preferred as they are more easily detected if they become loose. Nylon filaments are porous and quickly lose their stiffness in wet conditions, and inferior materials may even distort in hot water.

Mechanical equipment

These include floor scrubbers, rotating washers, power washers, air lines, steam cleaners, vacuum pick-ups and dishwashing and tray-cleaning machinery. Judicious use of mechanical equipment can significantly reduce labour requirements, but considerable care should be taken in selection to ensure that it is suitable for the use intended.

Gel or foam cleaning can improve performance

DISINFECTION

Although cleaning may remove large numbers of microorganisms, it does not kill them. The process which is used to destroy microorganisms is known as disinfection. Normally, disinfection is carried out after cleaning, although sometimes the two processes are combined, when a sanitizer is used.

Disinfection is 'the destruction of microorganisms, but not usually bacterial spores; it may not kill all microorganisms but reduces them to a level which is neither harmful to health nor the quality of perishable foods'. Disinfection may be achieved by using heat, chemicals, irradiation or u/v radiation. The term sterilization relates to the destruction of all microorganisms and spores and is normally unnecessary and impracticable to achieve within the food industry.

Heat disinfection

The application of heat is the most reliable and effective means of destroying microorganisms, although it may not be the most practical, especially for surfaces. It is used in machines, such as dishwashing machines, with a water temperature of 88°C and a contact time varying from 15 to 90 seconds. It is also used in sterilizing units where articles may be fully immersed for a period of 30 seconds at 82°C.

Steam disinfection of a can opener

Steam disinfection

Lances producing steam jets may be used to disinfect machinery or surfaces which are difficult to reach. Steam-cleaned equipment is self-drying.

Chemical disinfection

Disinfectants suitable for use in the food industry are limited to those which, when used correctly, will not, at the concentrations used, have a deleterious effect on equipment, personnel or food. Types of chemical disinfectants available include: chlorine release agents, such as bleach; quaternary ammonium compounds; and alcohols. Adequate contact time, prior to rinsing, is essential for effective disinfection.

Where to disinfect

Disinfection is usually only necessary for those surfaces where the presence of microorganisms, at the levels found, will have an adverse effect on the safety or quality of the food handled. Disinfection should normally be restricted to:

♦   food-contact surfaces;
♦   hand-contact surfaces;
♦   cleaning materials and equipment;
♦   the surface of fruit and vegetables to be consumed raw; and
♦   the hands (only when essential).

As microorganisms are rarely mobile and need to be physically carried onto food, the disinfection of non-food contact surfaces, such as floors and walls, is rarely necessary. Surfaces not directly coming into contact with food, but which are frequently touched by food handlers, need disinfecting to avoid the build-up of microorganisms on hands.

Hand disinfection

Hand disinfection increases the risk of dermatitis and is only necessary in aseptic conditions or to protect food handlers such as fish filleters from developing septic cuts. In the majority of food handling situations frequently washing the hands properly in warm water, using a liquid soap, is quite satisfactory. If hand disinfection is considered necessary it should be carried out after normal handwashing. Hand disinfectants should be fast-acting, dry rapidly and contain ingredients to protect the skin.

Disinfection of cleaning equipment and materials

Cleaning equipment is often an important vehicle of contamination and equipment used for hand or food contact surfaces should be disinfected frequently. Normal machine laundering at 65°C or above, in the case of cloths and towels, will achieve this. Floor mops should be thoroughly washed in hot water and detergent, squeezed to remove excess water and left to air dry. Wet mops should never be left in buckets or soaking in liquid overnight.

Disinfection frequency and effectiveness

In most operations, contamination by microorganisms takes time to build up to a significant level unless extraneous contamination is introduced by poor operational practice. Under normal circumstances, therefore, disinfection can correspond with cleaning intervals dictated by visual soiling or with work cycles. However, intermediate disinfection may be needed to counter the effects of inherent bad practice, such as the use of the same surface or equipment for cooked and raw meats. Effectiveness of disinfection is determined by bacteriological monitoring (swabbing) and ATP (adenosine triphosphate), not by visual inspection.

PROCEDURES AND METHODS OF CLEANING

Whatever the location, industry, soiling type or circumstances, cleaning and disinfection comprises six basic stages:

♦ pre-clean: sweeping, wiping or scraping off loose debris, pre-rinsing and/or pre-soaking;
♦ main clean: applying detergent and loosening of the main body of dirt;
♦ intermediate rinse: removal of loosened dirt, chemical neutralization of cleaning agent residues;
♦ disinfection: destruction of residual microorganisms;
♦ final rinse: removal of disinfectant residues; and
♦ drying: removal of final rinse water.

In the absence of visible soiling, the pre-clean may be omitted. The main clean and disinfection can take place in combination using specific chemicals known as sanitizers. (This becomes a three-stage process, i.e. main clean/sanitize, rinse and dry. Where there is no risk of taint the rinse may be unnecessary.) Drying can either be natural, as in air drying, or physical, using disposable paper towels, hot air or a clean dry cloth.

Manual dishwashing

Manual dishwashing is only recommended for washing-up in catering premises, public houses and retail outlets selling high-risk foods, when suitable dishwashing machines are not available. It also applies to food-processing, packing and distribution plants where small items are handwashed. Thermal disinfection is most effective if double sinks are used but a suitable chemical disinfectant, such as hypochlorite in a tablet form may be used, to minimize condensation problems and health and safety risks. However, the rinse water should still be hot enough to allow air drying. The full, six-stage procedure should always be followed:

♦ remove any heavy or loose soil by scraping and rinsing in cold water
♦ place articles in the first sink in detergent solution at 53°C to 55°C, scrub with a nylon brush and/or wipe with a clean cloth to loosen dirt residues;
♦ re-immerse in the first sink to wash off loosened dirt;
♦ place articles in the second sink to rinse off detergent;
♦ leave for sufficient time at a high enough temperature to ensure rapid air drying. Baskets for disinfecting purposes should be maintained in good condition and inspected regularly. They should be loaded so that all surfaces of crockery and equipment are fully exposed to the rinse water. Hollow items such as cups should be placed on their side; and
♦ remove articles, allow to drain and evaporate dry on a clean, disinfected surface.

A rinse aid may be added to the rinse water to promote smear-free drying. Items should then be removed and stacked in a clean, protected area ready for re-use. Containers and pans should be stored inverted to minimize the risk of contamination.

Mechanical dishwashing

Mechanical dishwashing is preferable to, and often more economic than, manual washing, provided the machine is used according to the manufacturer's instructions. Machines, in addition to cleaning, are also a highly efficient means of disinfecting small items of equipment and should be used for articles such as the removable parts of slicing machines, polypropylene chopping boards and other items which come into contact with high-risk foods, provided that no damage to the item will result. The sequence is as follows:

♦   remove excess food into suitable waste bins; if necessary pre-soak or spray, unless the machine is fitted with a pre-wash cycle;

♦   pack articles in a neat, orderly fashion so that items do not overlap, place in the machine and operate the wash cycle of hot detergent solution (49°C to 60°C), unless automatic;

♦   operate the rinse cycle (82°C to 88°C), with injection of rinse aid; and

♦   remove racks, allow cleaned items to drain and evaporate dry.

As a rule-of-thumb guide to the efficiency of a machine, if items coming out are too hot to handle and dry rapidly to a clean, smear-free finish, then the machine is operating correctly.

Cleaning a cooked meat slicing machine

Pre-clean:

♦   switch off power socket and remove the plug;

♦   set the slice thickness control to zero;

♦   dismantle the machine, pre-clean and pass removed parts through the dish-washing machine. Alternatively, thoroughly clean removed parts in a sink using detergent and hot water at 55°C and then disinfect in second sink or using a chemical disinfectant. Where the machine is of a type that has a removable blade, a blade guard must be fitted before the blade is removed. Cleaning may then commence, with the proviso that no person may clean a slicer or other dangerous machine unless they have reached their eighteenth birthday and have been properly trained; and

♦   clean and disinfect the machine carriage using clean cloths, taking particular care with the electrical parts.

Post-clean:

♦   reassemble the machine very carefully to avoid possible accidents;

♦   disinfect parts handled or otherwise contaminated;

♦   check the guards are properly fitted, reconnect the power and switch on the machine. Test run to check safe working. This procedure is vital because accidents have been caused by guards having been improperly fitted after cleaning. If any adjustments have to be made, the machine should be switched off and disconnected and the test run repeated;

♦ switch off the machine, disconnect the plug and cover with a freshly laundered tea towel or other suitable covering; and

♦ supervisor to check.

Cleaning schedules

Cleaning schedules must be clearly and concisely written, without ambiguity, to ensure that instructions to staff are easy to follow and result in the objective of the schedule being achieved.

Written schedules should specify:

♦ what is to be cleaned;

♦ who is to clean it;

♦ when it is to be cleaned (frequency);

♦ how it is to be cleaned;

Cleaning schedules should prevent dirt and dust build-up and other cleaning problems

♦ the time necessary to clean it;

♦ the chemicals (and dilution), materials and equipment to be used, and the contact time necessary;

♦ the safety precautions to be taken;

♦ the protective clothing to be worn; and

♦ who is responsible for monitoring and recording that it has been cleaned.

Supervisors should ensure that, after each cleaning session, all items specified in the schedule have been cleaned satisfactorily and any equipment that has been dismantled is safe to use.

Key points

♦ Effective cleaning and disinfection of food premises and equipment is essential to secure food safety.

♦ Negligent cleaning results in cross-contamination and may be a contributory factor in food poisoning outbreaks.

♦ Detergents are used to remove dirt and grease.

♦ Disinfectants are used to reduce microorganisms to a safe level.

♦ Staff involved in cleaning must be trained.

♦ Disinfection of food and hand-contact surfaces is essential.

♦ Cleaning equipment must be cleaned and disinfected after use.

♦ Cleaning schedules are essential to ensure effective cleaning and will assist a due diligence defence.

10 Pest control

Pest control is essential to prevent the spread of disease, although there are many other reasons for controlling pest infestations of food premises, including:

♦ to prevent the contamination of food by rodents or birds which may result in food poisoning. Rodents are scavengers and will feed on refuse, waste and unfit food. Rats often live in sewers and in close association with animals. They often carry food poisoning bacteria, such as salmonellae, both inside and outside their bodies and on their feet and in their mouths. When entering food premises, they can easily transfer food poisoning bacteria to food and food-contact surfaces from their fur, feet, mouths, urine and droppings;

♦ to prevent contact with rat urine which may result in Weil's disease;

♦ to prevent the wastage of food by contamination, and losses due to pest damage of packaging;

♦ to avoid the costs associated with loss of production, recall of contaminated food or defending criminal or civil action as a result of selling contaminated products;

♦ to prevent damage caused by gnawing. Electrical fires, burst pipes and subsidence, caused by burrowing, may all result from rodent infestation;

♦ to comply with the law and avoid possible closure of the food business;

♦ to avoid losing customers who object to pest infested premises or the sale of contaminated food; and

♦ to avoid losing staff who will not want to work in infested premises.

The common pests found in the food industry include:

♦ rodents: rats and mice;

♦ insects: flies, wasps, cockroaches, psocids, silverfish, stored product insects and ants;

♦ birds: mainly feral pigeons and sparrows and occasionally seagulls; and

♦ mites.

Rodents

The two most common rodents encountered in food premises are the Brown Rat and the House Mouse. The Black Rat is rarely encountered.

The Norway Rat (Brown Rat)

This is the predominant rat in the United Kingdom. It usually lives in burrows in the soil, especially beneath buildings, but may also be found in sewers, food stores, on farms and rubbish dumps. The Norway Rat is omnivorous but prefers cereals. One pair of adult rats can produce hundreds of offspring within a year but fortunately many do not survive. It is essential to destroy lone invaders of food premises as a pair of established rats can soon become a major infestation.

The House Mouse

The House Mouse is normally found living in buildings which provide it with harbourage, warmth, food and nesting materials. The House Mouse is omnivorous and a pair of adult mice can produce 2,000 young within a year, with the help of their offspring.

Signs of infestation

Certain members of staff should be specifically trained to identify evidence of pests. Cleaners are ideally suited for this purpose and should look for signs both inside and externally. Signs of infestation include:

- ♦ droppings: if very recent they are shiny and soft;
- ♦ the animals themselves, either dead or alive;
- ♦ gnawing marks and damage, for example, holes in sacks;
- ♦ holes and nesting sites;
- ♦ rat runs in undergrowth or smears around pipes;
- ♦ smear marks from the animal's coat;
- ♦ the loss of small amounts of food; and
- ♦ footprints in dust.

Insects

Insect pests can attack and destroy large amounts of food which becomes contaminated with bodies, webbing and excreta. Furthermore, cockroaches and flies may transmit food poisoning organisms to high-risk food. No food is completely safe from insect attack; however, beans, cereals, flour and dried fruits are among the most susceptible to infestation.

Flies

Many types of fly can cause problems in the food industry including the Housefly, the Bluebottle and the Fruit Fly. Many pathogens have been isolated from flies, including salmonella, *E. coli* O157, campylobacter, listeria and rotavirus. Flies infect our food in four ways:

- ♦ to feed they vomit partly digested food from the previous meal;
- ♦ they continually defecate;
- ♦ they carry bacteria on the hairs on their body and legs; and
- ♦ pupal cases, eggs, maggots and dead bodies end up in our food.

Typical breeding sites for houseflies are refuse and decaying organic matter. The female housefly lays around 600 eggs and it takes less than two weeks to go from egg to maggot to pupa to adult in warm weather.

Blowflies usually breed on decaying matter of animal origin, especially meat.

Fruit Flies generally occur in bakeries or fruit canning factories and beer cellars, and some lay their eggs in unwashed milk bottles. Control usually involves removal of the breeding material.

Wasps

Wasps may contaminate food by transferring bacteria from their legs or bodies. They are a major nuisance in premises such as bakeries, during the late summer.

The Wasp

Cockroaches

The two species of cockroach widely distributed in the United Kingdom are the Oriental Cockroach and the German Cockroach.

The Oriental Cockroach

The adults grow to about 24mm long and are shiny dark brown to black. They can climb rough vertical surfaces, such as brickwork, and are frequently found in cellars, kitchens, bakeries, hotels and drains. External

The Oriental Cockroach

survival and breeding, for example, in gardens, is possible.

The eggs are laid inside a case and take about two months to hatch at 25°C but this period is extended in cooler conditions. The female can produce over 150 eggs in its lifetime and it takes between six and 12 months to reach the adult stage in heated buildings with good food supplies.

The German Cockroach (Steam Fly)

The adult grows to about 15mm long and is yellowish brown. It can climb smooth painted walls and prefers the warm moist conditions found in kitchens, bakeries and especially ships' galleys. The female can produce around 300 eggs in its life span of three to 12 months.

Cockroach habits

Cockroaches live in groups and are omnivorous, nocturnal insects that give off an unpleasant characteristic odour. During the day they usually hide in cracks and crevices and their presence is usually detected by faecal pellets or their smell. Neither species fly. Over 40 pathogenic organisms have been isolated from cockroaches including food poisoning organisms.

Psocids or Booklice

Psocids are small (1mm to 2mm) cream, light brown or dark brown insects which are omnivorous and commonly infest flour, grain, nuts, chocolate, fish and meat products. They also feed on moulds and yeasts and infestations may be associated with packaging materials and pallets. The presence of booklice usually indicates conditions of high humidity.

Stored product insects

This is a large group of insects which attack foodstuffs in storage, transport and manufacture. It includes beetles, weevils, moths and their larvae. Dried products, cereals, flour, beans and nuts may all be attacked.

Pharaoh's Ant

Pharaoh's Ants are yellow/pale brown and approximately 2mm in length. Infestations usually occur in permanently heated buildings, especially hospitals, bakeries, hotels and residential property where they are often found in seemingly impenetrable food containers. All kinds of food may be attacked, although there is a preference for sweet and high protein food. Nests are difficult to detect and destroy. Physical transmission of pathogens to food is possible as they may visit drains, excreta and soiled dressings.

Bird pests

Birds which commonly gain access to food premises are sparrows, feral pigeons and starlings. Gulls are becoming an increasing problem, though rarely enter buildings. Warehouses and large food factories are prime targets although bakeries and supermarkets may also be affected.

Reasons for control
- to prevent the contamination of food or equipment by droppings, bodies, feathers and nesting materials;
- to prevent the transmission of food poisoning organisms;
- to remove sources of insect and mite infestation provided by nests, excreta and the birds themselves;
- to prevent blockages of gutters which may result in flooding and expensive maintenance;
- to prevent defacement of buildings (bird droppings produce an acid which attacks stone);
- to prevent roosting on fire escapes and similar structures, which may result in a safety hazard for human occupants; and
- to prevent damage to food packaging.

Pest control

Every food business should carry out integrated pest management, i.e. a control programme involving a series of integrated measures to control pests. Pests require food, shelter and security. Denial of these factors is known as environmental control and is the first and most important control measure intended to prevent infestation.

Environmental control

Environmental control may be considered as denial of:

♦ access – by design, maintenance and proofing of buildings; and
♦ food and harbourage – by good housekeeping.

Design, maintenance and proofing of buildings

Pests gain access to food premises in various ways. They may enter through open windows or doors, through gaps and cavities in the structure of the building or they may be brought in with food, packaging material or even laundry. Buildings must be designed and maintained to avoid undisturbed areas which can provide harbourage for pests. False ceilings, boxing, ducting, ovens and elevators must always be accessible for inspection and treatment. Cavities in internal walls or between surface finishes and

walls must be eliminated or effectively sealed. Service pipes or conduits passing through walls should be cemented in position.

All structural damage which provides access for pests must be repaired immediately and gaps around pipework must be sealed. Defective drains should be made good.

All buildings should be adequately proofed; doors should be self-closing and provided with metal kick plates,

Poor maintenance will allow pest entry

ventilation stacks should be provided with wire balloons and all ventilation openings, including opening windows (where there is a risk of infestation) must be adequately proofed to avoid pests gaining access. If a pencil can pass through a gap so can a young mouse.

All sources of water, such as dripping taps, defective gutters and leaks should be repaired and puddles removed.

Good housekeeping

If a pest breaches the first stage of the defences, i.e. proofing and maintenance, as well as inspection of raw materials, then good housekeeping will reduce the risk of the lone invader becoming a major infestation. In particular, it is important to ensure that:

♦ premises are kept in a clean and tidy condition to reduce sources of food harbourage and nesting material;
♦ cleaners do not remove or reposition bait boxes;
♦ spillages are cleared away promptly;
♦ food is kept in pest-proof containers and lids are always replaced;

- stock is stored and rotated correctly;
- undisturbed areas of unused equipment are checked frequently;
- adequate provision is made for the disposal of waste and areas are kept clean and tidy with tight-fitting lids being provided and used;
- as far as practicable, areas around the premises are kept free of harbourage and pests;
- all raw materials, including food, packaging and equipment, are checked to ensure they are not bringing pests into the premises;
- storage areas are regularly inspected and cleaned. Goods should be stored off the floor in well-lighted and ventilated areas. Old stock and new stock should, as far as practicable, segregated; and
- staff are alert and well trained. Regular audits are undertaken.

Physical and chemical control methods are necessary when environmental control has not succeeded.

Physical control methods

Physical control methods are usually preferred as the pest is caught, either dead or alive, and consequently is not able to die in some inaccessible place and the dead body will not contaminate food. Furthermore, physical control methods can be used during food production. Examples of physical control include rodent traps which can be baited or unbaited, electronic flying insect killers which use ultra-violet light to attract insects which are then caught on increasingly popular glue boards or electrocuted on charged grids (catch trays for dead insects should be emptied frequently and units should never be positioned above food or food equipment), sticky fly papers (which should not be used in public areas), cockroach traps (useful for monitoring the extent of infestations and the success of chemical treatments), mist nets for birds and bird scaring devices.

Catch trays must be emptied frequently

Chemical control methods

Unfortunately, although physical control methods may catch the occasional invader, they are usually unsuitable for dealing with major pest infestations, which have to be destroyed as quickly as possible.

Rodenticides are used in bait boxes and modern formulations can be provided in solid blocks or in a paste formulation to avoid problems from spillage and reduce the risk of food contamination.

The key to effective chemical control is to identify the insect and then determine which is the most vulnerable stage in its life cycle. Knock-down and residual insecticides of low toxicity can be used to control insects. Before use, all food and, where practicable, equipment should be removed and after treatment, work surfaces must be thoroughly cleaned and pests removed before food production commences. Particular care is necessary to avoid food contamination if aerosol fly spray is used by food handlers. (Indiscriminate control by food handlers is not good practice.)

A range of insecticidal dusts, baits, gels and sprays may be used to control most pests if care is taken to avoid contamination of food. Most treatments rely on the insects walking over the formulation and ingesting or absorbing a lethal dose. The continuous use of residual insecticides is not recommended in food rooms because of the risk of dead insects dropping into food. However, they may be useful in non-food rooms.

Fumigation of product is usually the only successful way to control infestations within commodities, although severe infestations may require the destruction of the product because of contamination with dead bodies.

Narcotizing of birds using alphachloralose, which is a stupefying substance, may be successful as any protected species can be released and the pest species collected and humanely destroyed.

It is essential that chemical control is undertaken by trained staff from either local authorities or specialist contractors. Safety precautions must be taken to comply with Health and Safety legislation. As soon as an infestation is discovered, immediate advice must be obtained.

The use of a pest control contractor

When selecting a pest control company, apart from the cost of the service, the following points should be taken into consideration:

♦ the type of pests you wish to control and the company's competency to deal with them;
♦ the ability to give 24-hour cover and provide an emergency call-out service;
♦ the use of suitably trained and discreet staff, with experience of the food industry;
♦ the frequency of the visits;
♦ the methods and materials to be used;
♦ if the company is a member of an appropriate professional association;
♦ the ability to provide a written report, including recommendations; and
♦ the adequacy of appropriate insurance cover regarding product, public and employees' liability.

The employment of a contractor does not absolve the company from overall responsibility for the conditions of the premises and food. However, it would most likely assist if a 'due diligence' defence was being relied upon.

BROWN RAT

BABY HOUSE MICE

RODENT TEETH MARKS

RODENT DAMAGE

RODENT DAMAGE

SPILLAGE RESULTING FROM RODENT
DAMAGE OF SACKS

GERMAN COCKROACH

COCKROACH PATH

ORIENTAL COCKROACH

COCKROACH TRAP

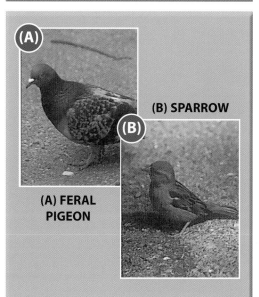

(A) FERAL PIGEON

(B) SPARROW

LARDER BEETLES AND LARVAE

LARVA OF FLOUR BEETLE

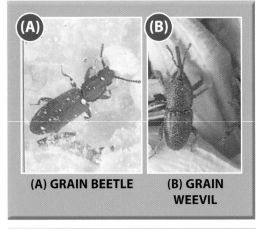

(A) GRAIN BEETLE   (B) GRAIN WEEVIL

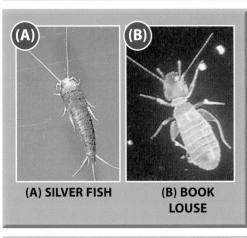

(A) SILVER FISH   (B) BOOK LOUSE

(A) GARDEN ANT   (B) PHARAOHS ANT

MILL MOTH

MILL MOTH LARVA

It is important that the following points are actioned:

♦ staff should be trained to recognize and report signs of infestation;
♦ an effective notification system should be in place to summon the contractor;
♦ the contractor should be accompanied during his/her visit;
♦ any unsatisfactory housekeeping should be noted;
♦ the position of bait boxes should be recorded;
♦ recommendations should be carried out quickly; and
♦ regular inspections of bait boxes should be made by nominated personnel.

Key points

♦ Rats, mice, flies and cockroaches are the most common pests of food premises.
♦ Pests can spread foodborne diseases.
♦ Infestations of pests may result in serious food complaints, prosecutions and the closure of the food business.
♦ Staff must be trained to identify evidence of pests which should be reported immediately.
♦ Environmental controls, i.e. preventing access and good housekeeping are the most cost-effective way of preventing infestations.
♦ Physical controls are preferred to avoid food contamination.
♦ Chemical controls should be applied by specialists.
♦ Integrated pest management is the key to successful control.

*All pest photographs used in this book were provided courtesy of Anticimex (Sweden) and Rentokil Initial plc.

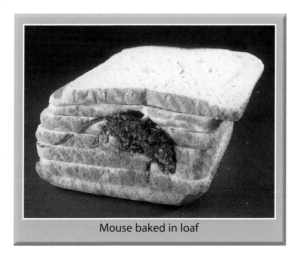

Mouse baked in loaf

11 *Supervisory management*

Supervisors and middle managers are an essential link in maintaining high standards of hygiene and preventing food poisoning. Their most important role is to ensure that food safety policies are implemented and the company's aims and objectives are achieved. Supervisors must communicate standards and ensure that staff are aware of their responsibilities. They should provide effective supervision, including motivation, instruction and on-the-job training to develop competency and control. Supervisors have a key role in the successful implementation of HACCP, or other food safety management systems. They must ensure that hazards are controlled, monitoring is effective and corrective action is taken in the event of failures. Supervisors should advise management when standards are being formulated and, in particular, ensure management are aware of the resources necessary to achieve the required standards.

Standards

Standards are necessary to ensure consistency and to provide a reference point to determine when a target has been achieved or a task, such as cleaning, has been completed satisfactorily. The term 'standard' may be used in several different ways. Voluntary standards, for example, hygiene or cleanliness, may be arbitrary levels; legal standards, such as storage temperatures for food and bacteriological standards, are obligatory minimum levels and international standards such as HACCP and ISO 9000 are recognised by many countries. Standards can relate to premises, people or products and include labelling and packaging.

Standards may be set by an individual, a company, customers, governments, trade associations and independent standards authorities. They are used to provide a uniform service or product which the customer expects. Premises with high standards develop a good reputation, which attracts new customers, with the minimum number of complaints. Food safety standards set above the minimum legal level will ensure compliance with the law, codes of practice and industry guides and the production of safe, wholesome food of acceptable quality and shelf-life. Standards are also essential to facilitate control, monitoring and auditing to assess compliance.

Specifications are documented standards which describe the safety and quality characteristics of the raw materials and the products obtained from suppliers. Specifications ensure uniformity and may include minimum standards for weight, size, colour, pH, a_w, absence or maximum numbers of microorganisms, processing requirements, delivery details, including temperature, absence of physical and chemical contaminants, packaging and labelling. They may also detail the action that will be taken, usually rejection, if the specification is not adhered to.

Food safety policies

When a company has determined its aim and objectives, the standards can be determined and incorporated into a food safety policy. The food safety policy can be used to attain good hygiene practices or good manufacturing practices which are essential prerequisites to the effective implementation of HACCP based systems. This document is also very useful to support a 'due diligence' defence and an effective way of communicating the required standards to staff and identifying training needs. To remain effective, the document should be reviewed regularly. A responsibility flow chart showing management structure and individual responsibilities with regard to hygiene should be included, together with the following:

- ♦ a commitment to produce safe food;
- ♦ a commitment to observe all relevant legal requirements, industry guides to good hygiene practice and government codes of practice;
- ♦ a commitment to identify hazards and implement effective control and monitoring procedures, especially at points critical to food safety and to review the hazard analysis system periodically and whenever the food business' operations change;
- ♦ staff training and the implementation of a planned food hygiene training programme (training records should be maintained);
- ♦ procedures to ensure that all food and water suppliers are satisfactory/approved (suppliers should provide a copy of their food safety policy and customer references);
- ♦ a commitment to provide the necessary premises, equipment, facilities and maintenance to achieve high standards of hygiene, including personal hygiene;
- ♦ satisfactory temperature control and monitoring systems for food ingredients and products during storage, preparation/processing, distribution and display. Procedures should be identified for safe alternatives if equipment is defective;
- ♦ systems to ensure satisfactory cleaning and, where necessary, disinfecting of the premises, equipment and facilities (cleaning schedules will be required);
- ♦ adequate pest control measures, including proofing, the use of specialist contractors and maintaining records;
- ♦ procedures and systems for health screening and the reporting of staff illness, dealing with visitors, contractors, enforcement officers, food poisoning incidents, customer complaints, delivery of raw materials, traceability and product recall, hazard warnings and waste management;
- ♦ effective quality assurance/control systems, including stock rotation, foreign body control, organoleptic assessment, sampling, food labelling and in-house audits. Procedures for removing unacceptable suppliers from the approved list; and
- ♦ a commitment to provide the resources for and training of managers to ensure the implementation, updating and enforcement of the policy throughout the business.

Quality assurance

Quality assurance may be considered as all the planned and systematic actions necessary to provide confidence that a product or service will satisfy the customer's requirements for quality over time. Many organizations have developed their own quality assurance systems and some of these may comply with the International Standards Organisation ISO 9000 series. Recognition for achieving the standard is through accredited certification bodies.

Quality control

Quality control is differentiated from quality assurance in that it is a series of techniques used to assess compliance with a standard specification by testing and product sampling. It is usually based on statistical criteria and often occurs on completion of production. In essence, it is a reactive process which identifies things that are wrong after the event and does not necessarily determine the cause of the problem.

Quality assurance is proactive and attempts to stop things going wrong in the first place. It is a continuous process of product assessment and fault correction throughout production and should be the responsibility of all staff. The effective implementation of quality assurance requires:

♦ the specification (what is to be done);
♦ documented instruction (how it is to be done);
♦ the recording system (to confirm it has been done); and
♦ a monitoring system (to confirm recording and corrective actions are satisfactory).

Quality must be built into a food product it cannot be inspected into it.

The inspection of food premises

An inspection of a food premises or operation will only be effective if the person undertaking the inspection has a clear understanding of the reason for inspection and also has the relevant technical knowledge, skills and experience. The inspection must be planned and sufficient time must be allowed to achieve the objective. After the inspection, the data collected will need to be analyzed to determine the action to be taken to rectify any defects. A comprehensive report should be written and problems must be followed up to ensure compliance. An inspection involves careful observation and examination whereas an audit may be considered as comparing what you actually do with what you say you do. The two processes will usually overlap.

Knowledge required

The inspector must have a thorough understanding of:

♦ all technical aspects of the operation, for example, catering practice, cook-chill or canning;

- the legal requirements and relevant codes of practice or industry guides;
- the main causes of food poisoning and complaints associated with the type of operation;
- all relevant aspects of HACCP; and
- the industry norm, i.e. standards expected for similar premises.

Purpose of the inspection

There are many different reasons for inspecting a premises, including:

- to ensure that the premises/operation is capable of producing safe food;
- to assess the effectiveness of HACCP, especially in relation to critical control points;
- to check that standards have been achieved;
- to identify the training needs of staff;
- to provide advice;
- to demonstrate management commitment to food safety;
- to respond to a complaint; and
- to re-visit.

Stages in the inspection

(1) Planning and preparation

Having decided on the objectives of the inspection, the scope and depth can be determined. The inspection may consider microbiological, chemical and physical hazards and it may be a full or part inspection or very specific.

The equipment required will include a probe thermometer, torch, protective clothing, sample bags, a scraper and an A4 pad and clipboard. The inspector may need additional knowledge and training to develop inspection skills, including interviewing, simulation/reconstruction, measurement, analyzing and report writing.

Prior to undertaking the inspection, it is useful to have records of previous inspections, specifications, hazards, risks, relevant legislation, industry guides and codes of practice. Access to monitoring records relating to customer complaints, pests and cleaning, together with the HACCP plan and site layout, would also be beneficial. To be effective, checklists should be designed specifically for the premises being inspected, although aide-memoires may be even more useful.

(2) Conducting the inspection

The timing of the inspection will be dictated by the objective. If undertaking a comprehensive inspection, it is necessary to examine each step in the production of food from the receipt of deliveries to the serving of customers. The hazards (contamination, multiplication and survival) controls, monitoring and corrective action at each stage (critical control point) should be considered.

Observations should be carried out as inconspicuously as possible and the inspection should be methodical. A typical routine involves starting at a defined point, such as the wash-hand basin, within a room, the progressive examination of all relevant items around the perimeter and then the same ordered examination of central fittings, installation or equipment.

The inspection should be thorough. Every aspect of the subject under examination should be covered. It may not be enough to look at a piece of equipment; it may need to be dismantled and/or moved from its position. Cupboards and refrigerators may need to be wholly or partially emptied and surfaces may need to be scraped or tapped to assess soundness. In this respect, full use should be made of the senses: sight, smell, hearing and touch.

(3) Analysing the data

All of the raw data collected during the inspection will need careful analysis to provide meaningful information which can be presented in the report. For example: several cleaning defects in differing rooms may indicate inappropriate cleaning schedules; if staff are wearing dirty protective clothing this may result from poor communication and/or poor supervision or training; several empty paper towel or soap dispensers may demonstrate ineffective monitoring as well as poor management commitment to achieving high standards of personal hygiene; food hygiene certificates may be hung on the wall, but the staff may not be competent to undertake their activities and to produce safe food.

(4) Report

The report of the inspection should be more than just a list of faults. Good practice and achievements should be complimented. Faults should be grouped together, for example, personal hygiene or cleaning. The remedial work should be prioritized, for example, an unsafe process should be dealt with at the time of the inspection, some cleaning problems may need to be rectified within a day, whereas some decoration, structural items or replacement equipment may be dealt with in one to three months.

Recommendations and legal requirements should be clearly distinguished, and any solutions proposed should be cost-effective and practical.

Inspection by an enforcement officer

In the event of an inspection by an enforcement officer, the supervisor or manager should make the officer welcome and answer his/her questions accurately and honestly. A plan of the premises should be available, together with all relevant monitoring records. The officer will be interested in the food safety policy and any HACCP documentation provided.

It is usual for the officer to be accompanied throughout the inspection. If you do not understand the reason for a request or, for example, why a particular process is considered to be a risk, you should always ask for an explanation.

At the conclusion of the inspection, it is advisable to keep a record of any work that must be completed immediately and also the follow-up action, if any, the officer intends to take. Priorities and timescales for completing any remedial work should be noted.

Staff training
The objectives of hygiene training
The main objective of hygiene training is to change the behaviour and attitude of food handlers at work and so minimize the risk of food poisoning and food complaints. To achieve this objective, staff will need to be provided with the knowledge and skills to operate hygienically and then motivated and supervised to ensure that they implement what they have learned. Training should not be undertaken haphazardly but must be carefully planned. The most effective way of undertaking hygiene training is to develop and implement a training programme, the principles of which are applicable to all businesses, although the programme will be less formal for smaller businesses.

The benefits of hygiene training
Training contributes significantly to the profitability of a food business by:
♦ assisting in the production of safe food;
♦ safeguarding the quality of the product and reducing food wastage;
♦ reducing complaints;
♦ generating a pride in appearance and practices, increasing job satisfaction and probably reducing staff turnover;
♦ contributing to increased productivity;
♦ ensuring that all the correct procedures, including cleaning, are followed;
♦ complying with any legal provisions or the requirements of industry guides or codes of practice;
♦ promoting a good company image which should result in increased business; and
♦ improving the supervisory skills of managers.

Training methods
There are many ways of ensuring that food handlers are effectively trained depending on the type of business, their level of hygiene knowledge and their literary skills. Continuous on-the-job instruction and control by a knowledgeable supervisor is essential. A large number of visual aids are available to enhance training sessions or reinforce important messages. Videos, overhead transparencies, books, leaflets, posters and computer-based training packages are all useful, especially if the audience finds them enjoyable. Humorous illustrations are more memorable than text. Interactive training packages and training sessions, for example, group exercises, quiz books, software, games and role playing, produce better results.

The legal requirement for training
Food business operators are to ensure that:
♦ food handlers are supervised and instructed and/or trained in food hygiene matters commensurate with their work activity; and

- those responsible for the development and maintenance of the food safety management system based on the HACCP principles, or for the operation of the relevant guides have received adequate training in the application of the HACCP principles.

It is recommended that:
- all food handlers receive written or verbal instruction in the essentials of food hygiene before they start work and additional hygiene awareness instruction within four weeks of starting work;
- food handlers who prepare open high-risk foods or have a supervisory role receive Foundation training within three months of starting work; and
- supervisors undertake Intermediate training (12 to 24 hours) or Advanced training (24 to 40 hours duration), depending on their actual duties. Supervisors and managers should also undertake relevant HACCP training.

Training programme and records

It is good practice for food businesses to have a training programme which identifies the training needs of each food handler. Records of training, to include induction (hygiene essentials), hygiene awareness, Foundation, Intermediate or Advanced, any specific courses attended, such as HACCP, and refresher training, should be completed for each food handler to assist compliance with the legal requirements and to assist in establishing a 'due diligence' defence (It must always be remembered that the law requires competency for food handlers to produce safe food, not an ageing certificate on the wall).

THE INVESTIGATION OF FOOD POISONING OUTBREAKS

The effective investigation of food poisoning outbreaks is essential to limit the spread of infection and to provide information:
- for the food industry on unsafe products and practices;
- to improve the effectiveness of inspections by enforcement officers; and
- to use when formulating new legislation.

In the event of a serious or large outbreak, an outbreak control team is usually established. A food poisoning outbreak control team consists of several experts, including a consultant in public health medicine, a microbiologist and an environmental health officer.

The objectives of an investigation are to:
- contain the spread of illness;
- identify the outbreak location (place where food vehicle was prepared or served);
- identify the food vehicle (food eaten which gave rise to the illness) and prevent further sales;

♦ identify the causative agent involved, for example, *Salmonella* Enteritidis, norovirus, a poisonous chemical or a toxic plant;
♦ trace cases/carriers, especially food handlers;
♦ trace the source of the causative agent;
♦ determine the main faults that contributed to the outbreak, for example, food left at ambient temperatures for several hours;
♦ make recommendations to prevent recurrence; and
♦ provide data for use in surveillance.

The role of the environmental health officer

In addition to his/her involvement with the outbreak control team, the environmental health officer uses his/her skills in tracing cases and persons at risk, organizing the collection of specimens and interviewing people involved to obtain information to assist with achieving the above objectives.

When the outbreak location has been identified, the investigating officer will undertake a comprehensive investigation and inspection of the operation to ascertain the faults in the food preparation and the management failures that resulted in the faults. If the evidence suggests the sale of unfit food and the absence of a 'due diligence' defence, the officer may also collect evidence for use in legal proceedings.

The officer will need to secure the assistance of the manager and/or supervisor to assist in the investigation. In the event of a very recent outbreak, the officer will request the suspension of cleaning and disinfection and, perhaps, the termination of food production or even the closure of the food premises.

The officer will require details of:
♦ all food production staff and their functions;
♦ staff sickness records, including staff with septic cuts or boils; and
♦ all relevant food production details.

The officer may require samples of food and meal or packaging remains. Swabs of surfaces and equipment may be taken. Staff will be interviewed and asked to provide faecal specimens.

The role of the supervisor

If a supervisor suspects the business may have been responsible for a food poisoning outbreak, he/she should advise the manager, who will probably require any further food sales to be suspended, if the outbreak is very recent, until the allegation has been investigated. Any staff with boils or septic cuts or who have recently suffered from diarrhoea or vomiting, even if they are now symptom-free, should be sent to the doctor and not resume food handling duties until medical clearance has been obtained.

Checks should be made to ensure that no other similar complaints have been received. Supervisors may be able to obtain invaluable information on the history of the suspect foods from delivery to service. In the case of retail or manufacturing, recall procedures for suspect food may need implementing.

Supervisors will be able to assist in the provision of necessary information for the environmental health officer. Records provided by management may be slightly out of date because of last minute changes and the supervisor will need to check the accuracy, especially of menus, supplier lists, staff work and sickness records, methods of preparation and persons at risk.

Supervisors will also be given the task of ensuring the premises are thoroughly cleaned and disinfected once the environmental health officer is satisfied that they are capable of producing safe food. In addition any recommendations from the environmental health officer on preventing future outbreaks will need to be implemented.

The role of the consultant in communicable disease control (CCDC)

CCDCs are public health doctors employed by the health authorities and who work for local authorities. They are responsible for controlling public health diseases, including food poisoning, and usually chair the outbreak control team. In addition to their medical skills, they often provide the epidemiological expertise and give advice on controlling infection and treatment required. They rarely get involved in enforcement matters or the inspection of premises.

The Health Protection Agency (HPA)

The HPA is a national organizaton for England and Wales, created on 1st April 2003 to protect people's health by minimizing risks from infectious diseases, poisons, chemicals, biological and radiation hazards. The HPA incorporates several organizations including, the Public Health Laboratory Service, the Communicable Disease Surveillance Centre, the Central Public Health Laboratory and NHS public health staff responsible for infectious disease control.

The HPA is responsible for:
◆ advising the Government on public health matters;
◆ delivering services to protect public health;
◆ providing impartial advice and information to professionals and the public;
◆ providing a rapid response to health protection emergencies; and
◆ improving knowledge of health protection through research, development, education and training.

HACCP (HAZARD ANALYSIS CRITICAL CONTROL POINT)

Food Safety Management and HACCP

Food businesses have a legal and moral responsibility to implement a food safety management system based on the codex principles of HACCP (hazard analysis critical control point).

HACCP was developed in the 1960's by the Pillsbury Company and NASA to guarantee the safety of food intended for astronauts. HACCP shifts the emphasis of control from end-product testing and inspection to identifying current and predicted hazards and risks and removing them prior to or during production. HACCP systems prioritise controls so that resources are concentrated on the points critical to food safety.

Terminology associated with HACCP

Codex Alimentarius: A collection of internationally adopted food standards and guidelines intended to protect the health of consumers and to ensure fair practices in food trade. (Produced by the Codex Alimentarius Commission of the Food and Agriculture Organisation of the United Nations and the World Health Organisation).

Control measures: Actions required to prevent or eliminate a food safety hazard or reduce it to an acceptable level.

Corrective action: The action to be taken when a critical limit is breached.

Critical control point: A step in the process at which control can be applied and is essential to prevent or eliminate a food safety hazard or reduce it to an acceptable level.

Critical limit: The value of a monitored action that separates the acceptable from the unacceptable.

Decision tree: A sequence of questions to determine if a step in the process is a critical control point.

Deviation: Failure to meet a critical limit.

Flow diagram: A systematic representation of the sequence of steps or operations involved with a particular food item or process, usually from receipt of raw materials to consumer.

Food safety management system: The policies, procedures, practices, controls and documentation that ensure the food sold by a food business is safe to eat and free from contaminants.

HACCP (hazard analysis critical control point): A food safety management system which identifies, evaluates and controls hazards which are significant for food safety.

HACCP team: A group of people with appropriate expertise who develop and implement a HACCP system.

Hazard: A biological, chemical or physical agent in, or condition of, food with the potential to cause harm (an adverse health effect) to the consumer. (NB most biological hazards are microbiological.)

Hazard analysis (Codex Alimentarius): The process of collecting and evaluating information on hazards and conditions leading to their presence to decide which are significant for food safety and therefore should be addressed in the HACCP plan.

Monitoring: The planned observations and measurements of control parameters to confirm that the process is under control and that critical limits are not exceeded.

Prerequisite programmes: The good hygiene practices that a food business must have in place before implementing HACCP to enable the HACCP plan to concentrate on the most significant hazards.

Risk: The likelihood of a hazard occurring in food.

Target level: The predetermined value for the control measure, which will eliminate or control the hazard at a control point.

Tolerance: The specified degree of latitude for a control measure, which if exceeded, requires immediate corrective action.

Validation: Obtaining evidence that elements of the HACCP plan are effective, especially the critical control points and critical limits.

Verification: The application of methods, procedures and tests, and other evaluations, in addition to the monitoring, to determine compliance with the HACCP plan. (Includes prerequisite programmes.)

The Codex Alimentarius 7 Principles of HACCP

HACCP as defined by Codex Alimentarius, is a food safety management system based on the following seven principles:

◆ conduct a hazard analysis. Prepare a flow diagram, identify the hazards and specify the control measures;

◆ determine the critical control points;

◆ establish critical limits;

◆ establish a system to monitor control of each CCP;

◆ establish corrective actions when monitoring indicates a particular CCP is not under control;

◆ establish procedures for verification to confirm that the HACCP system is working effectively; and

◆ establish documentation and records concerning all procedures appropriate to these principles and their application.

Prerequisite programmes for HACCP

Prior to the implementation of an effective HACCP system, a business must be operating in accordance with good hygiene practice or, in the case of factories, good manufacturing practice, and comply with all relevant food safety legislation. Management must be committed to the introduction of HACCP and provide adequate resources and suitable facilities. Prerequisite programmes should include:

◆ approved suppliers;

◆ premises and equipment well designed, constructed and maintained. Equipment should be calibrated. Product should flow from the delivery of raw ingredients to the production of finished products, without there being a risk of cross-contamination;

◆ water and ice used in food production must be potable;

◆ staff must be trained commensurate with their work activities; they should have high standards of personal hygiene, especially in relation to handwashing. A health and exclusion policy should exist to screen new employees and ensure that food handlers with diarrhoea and/or vomiting do not handle food until they are symptom-free for at least 48 hours and, when they return to work, they can be relied on to thoroughly wash their hands after

using the toilet;
♦ effective planned cleaning and disinfection and the use of cleaning schedules for monitoring purposes;
♦ integrated pest management;
♦ effective waste management;
♦ thorough washing and disinfecting of all ready-to-eat fruit and salad vegetables;
♦ stock rotation; and
♦ labelling, traceability and recall procedures.

Good hygiene practices prevent some microbiological contaminants and the majority of physical and chemical contaminants that could occur in catering and retailing operations.

The implementation of HACCP (12 logical steps)

1. Assemble and train the HACCP team

The HACCP team must be proportionate to the size, risk and complexity of the business. The team must be aware of the hazards, and controls associated with the production of food. In small businesses, one person may be the sole team member, although external consultants may also assist.

2. Describe the products or processes

A detailed description of each product will be required in manufacturing. However, in catering or retailing it is more likely that the processes will be used as a basis for the flow diagrams. For example, perishable raw food which is cooked and served hot or, high-risk food which is served cold.

3. Identify intended users

Especially vulnerable groups such as babies, the elderly, pregnant women, ill people, those who suffer allergic reactions and those with immune deficiency.

4. Construct a flow diagram

A flow diagram is a systematic representation of the sequence of steps involved with a particular food item or process, usually from purchase of raw materials to the consumer.

5. Validate the flow diagram

This involves ensuring that your theoretical flow diagram accurately reflects what happens in practice.

Flow diagram for perishable raw food, cooked and served hot or cold.

6. Conduct a hazard analysis (Principle 1)

Hazard analysis involves:

♦ identifying the hazards (what could go wrong?) that may affect the process;
♦ identifying the steps at which the hazards are likely to occur;
♦ deciding which hazards are significant, i.e. their elimination or reduction to acceptable levels is essential to the production of safe food; and
♦ determining the measures necessary to control the hazards (measures to prevent things going wrong).

Food safety hazards

Food safety hazards are biological, chemical or physical contaminants with the potential to cause harm to the person who consumes the contaminated food. The commonest biological hazards are microbiological.

Biological hazards include bacteria or their toxins, viruses, moulds and parasites that may cause foodborne illness. They involve:

♦ the contamination of ready-to-eat food by sufficient numbers of pathogens to cause illness;
♦ the multiplication of microorganisms; and
♦ the survival of microorganisms, for example, as a result of undercooking.

Poor temperature control or prolonged time at ambient temperature could result in any food poisoning bacteria multiplying to large numbers. A failure to cook thoroughly could result in the survival of some food poisoning bacteria.

Chemical hazards include poisonous foods such as toadstools, pesticides, cleaning chemicals and excess additives that can poison people. Allergens are usually considered as chemical hazards.

Physical hazards (foreign bodies) include glass, sharp metal objects and stones that may result in cuts to the mouth, broken teeth, choking and internal injury. Burning is also a physical hazard.

Physical or chemical hazards could occur at any stage in the process and it is unlikely that their removal will be guaranteed at a later stage.

Control measures

Control measures are the actions required to prevent or eliminate a food safety hazard or reduce it to an acceptable level, for example, cooking food to kill bacteria or keeping food cold in a refrigerator to stop the multiplication of bacteria. Control measures for physical contaminants include the use of metal detectors and filters and strict rules about the storage and use of chemicals.

7. Determine the critical control points (CCPs) (Principle 2)

These are steps in the process where control measures must be used to prevent food poisoning, injury or harm to the customer.

CCPs are identified by using judgement and expertise. Cooking, or processing, cooling and cold or hot storage (of high-risk foods) are usually CCPs.

8. Establish critical limits for each CCP (Principle 3)

Critical limits are values which are set for control measures to ensure the food is safe, for example, cooking to a centre temperature of 75°C, hot holding of food above 63°C or refrigerating food below 8°C. If a critical limit is breached, for example, if refrigerated food is above 8°C for more than 4 hours, the food should be thrown away. To avoid throwing food away and to allow remedial action to be taken before a critical limit is breached it is best to set a target level, for example, store food below 5°C or cook food to 78°C. If the target level is breached, for example, the food in the refrigerator is 7°C, the thermostat can be turned down to reduce the temperature before the critical limit is breached.

Critical limits include time, temperature, size, weight and appearance/colour. Objective and measurable parameters are preferable.

9. Monitoring (checking) of control measures at each CCP (Principle 4)

Monitoring is essential to confirm that the process is under control and critical limits are not exceeded. Monitoring also ensures:

◆   expected standards are being achieved;
◆   a due diligence defence will be assisted; and
◆   complaints are minimised and commitment and motivation of staff are improved.

Monitoring methods include organoleptic assessment, auditing, measuring temperatures/time/weight etc., visual inspections and checking records, and competency.

Monitoring systems should state **WHAT** the critical limits and target levels are; **HOW** the monitoring should be undertaken; **WHERE** the monitoring should be undertaken; **WHEN** the monitoring should be undertaken; and **WHO** is responsible for monitoring. The frequency of monitoring must be cost-effective and sufficient to ensure that the hazards are controlled.

Organoleptic assessment of food

The appearance, smell, texture, taste and other physical characteristics of food are valuable for obtaining a rapid assessment of food standards (quality, taint and spoilage). However, food contaminated by pathogenic bacteria may appear in all respects fit to eat and suspect food should not be tasted. Specific indicators include:

◆   **Smell** – good food should smell fresh, pleasant and natural. Unusual, stale, musty or rancid smells should invite suspicions. Chemical smells may indicate chemical contamination. Ammonia smells in some fish are an early sign of decomposition;

♦ **Taste** – unusual bitterness or sweetness, a soapy taste or any untypical flavour may indicate unfitness;

♦ **Appearance** – food should be visibly free from signs of spoilage, fungal growth, slime, darkening or other change in colour, untypical wetness and mechanical damage. Absence of foreign objects and dirt in finished goods, including pests, pest debris and parasites, is important. Meat, poultry and fish should be free from signs of disease or other pathological conditions. In frozen food excessive ice can be an indicator of mishandling, as can large ice crystals within the texture; loose foods such as peas should not be welded together. A final judgement of frozen food can only be made after defrosting;

♦ **Sound** – many packed foods, especially canned goods, emit a characteristic sound on being tapped or shaken. Any such food or pack emitting an untypical sound is suspect;

♦ **Texture** – unusual softness, hardness, brittleness or change in texture may be indicative of unfitness. Meat, fish and certain other products, such as cheese, should display a springy texture. Light pressure from a finger that causes an indentation to remain can be significant.

Bacteriological monitoring

Bacteriological monitoring can be used to assist the verification of HACCP or hazard analysis, but is also commonly used in manufacturing premises to:

♦ build up a profile of product quality;

♦ indicate trends in product quality;

♦ ascertain whether handling techniques are satisfactory;

♦ indicate product safety and the absence of specific organisms or pathogens;

♦ determine effectiveness of cleaning and disinfection;

♦ determine effectiveness of processing;

♦ confirm that legal standards or customer's specifications are being met.

However, bacteriological monitoring has the following disadvantages:

♦ it is usually retrospective and cannot be used to verify product safety where there is a short time between production and consumption, for example, in conventional catering or for products with short shelf-lives;

♦ it is relatively expensive;

♦ considerable expertise may be needed to interpret results and relate them to product age;

♦ the non-uniform distribution of bacteria in foods and the effect of different laboratory techniques and sampling methods significantly affect the results;

♦ the operation is being controlled by a laboratory technician who may be remote from the food production;

♦ only a limited number of samples can be taken;

♦ not all hazards are identified; and
♦ only a small section of the workforce assumes responsibility for product safety.

Monitoring of food handlers

Monitoring of food handlers by supervisors is essential to identify failures in personal hygiene or hygiene practices and to identify training needs. Monitoring can involve observation, for example, to ensure staff wash their hands properly when entering the food room and to ensure protective clothing is clean, put on and worn correctly. More formal monitoring can involve bacteriological swabbing of fingers, competency testing and annual medical checks by medical staff to reinforce rules relating to illness.

10. Establish corrective actions (Principle 5)

Corrective action is the action taken when a critical limit is breached. It involves two distinct parts: firstly, dealing with the affected product (for example, destroying the product or reducing the shelf-life), and secondly, bringing the process back under control (for example, adjusting the thermostat on the refrigerator or calling the engineer to repair equipment).

Procedures for corrective action should specify: the action to be taken; who should take the action; who should be notified; whether or not production/sales should continue; whether products should be recalled; how the product should be dealt with; and who can authorise the re-start of production or sales.

Manufacturers, wholesales and retailers should ensure that all products are clearly labelled and traceable in the event of a recall being necessary.

11. Establish verification procedures (prove that the HACCP system is working) (Principle 6)

Verification involves the use of methods, procedures and tests, in addition to those used in monitoring, to demonstrate that the HACCP system is working effectively. Auditing the HACCP system to ensure all hazards and CCPs have been identified and controls and monitoring remain effective is the most common verification technique. All scientific data on which the system is based can be re-examined to ensure it is still applicable. Monitoring records, deviations and complaints can be examined. Part of verification is validation i.e. obtaining evidence that elements of the HACCP plan are effective, especially the critical control points and critical limits.

Does the control eliminate the hazard, for example, evidence that the cooking or processing temperature and time is adequate to make the food safe?
The HACCP plan should be reviewed periodically and particularly if:
♦ a justified complaint is received or illness occurs;
♦ raw materials change e.g. fresh chicken instead of frozen;
♦ the recipe changes, e.g. salt is removed;
♦ equipment changes, e.g. a blast chiller is introduced; and
♦ packaging or distribution changes, e.g. refrigerated transport is utilised.

12. Establish documentation and record-keeping (Principle 7)

The amount and type of paperwork required to support HACCP systems should be proportionate to the size and type of food business and the risks involved with the process. Documentation is useful to demonstrate that food safety is being managed and, provided records are completed accurately at the appropriate time, they are useful to support a due diligence defence if this is required in court.

The documentation to support the HACCP study may include:

♦ the HACCP Plan;
♦ a floor plan;
♦ the prerequisite programmes;
♦ audit reports;
♦ the approved supplier list;
♦ monitoring records (such as: deliveries, training records, refrigerator and freezer temperatures, cleaning schedules, stock rotation, pest control and exclusion records). All monitoring records should be signed and dated. Obselete instructions/documentation must always be withdrawn

TEMPERATURE CHECK - COLD
Records for Week Commencing ..../........../...........

Fridge number/place	Saturday am	pm	Sunday am	pm	Monday am	pm	Tuesday am	pm	Wednesday am	pm	Thursday am	pm	Friday am	pm
Fridge one														
Fridge two														
Fridge three														
Fridge four														
Fridge five														
Supervisor's initials (am & pm)														

For any situations above 8°C, record action taken

Signature: .... Date...........

The HACCP Plan may include:

♦ details of the HACCP team;
♦ the scope and terms of reference;
♦ the product or process description;
♦ flow diagrams;
♦ consumers;
♦ hazard analysis and CCP determination;
♦ critical limits and targets, deviations and corrective actions; and
♦ validation, verification and review procedures.

Some of this documentation will be itemised on the HACCP control chart.

The following table is known as a HACCP control chart and includes examples of typical hazards, control measures, monitoring and corrective actions.

STEP	Hazards	Controls & critical limits	Monitoring	Corrective action*
PURCHASE	Contamination with harmful bacteria, toxic chemicals or foreign bodies.	Use only reputable suppliers. Select least hazardous ingredients. Product specification. Purchase branded products.	Ensure supplier has effective HACCP system and good hygiene practices. Obtain HACCP documentation. Inspect supplier's business. Utilise customer references.	Revisit/audit supplier's premises. Review product specification. Warn supplier. Change supplier.
DELIVERY	Contamination with harmful bacteria, toxic chemicals or foreign bodies.	Food covered/protected or in suitable containers. Deboxing area. Use only approved suppliers. Date codes/labels. Specific delivery requirements. (NOT with toxic chemicals.)	Internal audit (visual and sensory checks.) Condition of packaging/food. Conditions of vehicle/driver. Supplier on the approved supplier list. Food is within date code. Food is delivered in accordance with specification.	Change supplier. Review/reissue product specification/instructions. Refuse delivery. Return stock. Inform chef or manager. Review systems/training.
	Multiplication of food poisoning bacteria.	Chilled food below 5°C. (Critical limit 8°C.) Frozen food below −18°C. Move to storage within 15 minutes of unloading.	Temperature of food using calibrated probe thermometer. Time to move to storage.	
CHILLED STORAGE	Contamination with harmful bacteria, toxic chemicals or foreign bodies.	Food covered/protected. Segregation of raw and high-risk food. Use disinfected temperature probe. Food not stored in open cans. Load food correctly.	Internal audit. Condition of food. Condition of packaging.	Inform chef or manager. Discard unfit or out-of-date food. Review systems/training.
	Multiplication of food poisoning bacteria.	Chilled food below 5°C. (Critical limit >8°C for 2 hours.) Don't overload refrigerator. Good stock rotation procedures. Date codes/labels.	Air temperature. In-between pack temperature. Temperature of food. Time above 8°C. Door seals. Food is within date code.	Adjust thermostat. Reorganise refrigerator in order to allow good air circulation. Call out refrigerator engineer. Repair/replace fridge. Implement contingency plan.
FROZEN STORAGE	Multiplication of food poisoning bacteria.	Food frozen below −18°C.	Internal audit. Air temperature. In-between pack temperature. Temperature of food.	Inform chef or manager. Discard unfit or out-of-date food. Review systems/training. Adjust thermostat. Call out refrigerator engineer. Replace freezer. Implement contingency plan.
DRY STORAGE	Contamination with harmful bacteria, toxic chemicals or foreign bodies.	Food covered/protected or in suitable containers. Care in handling.	Internal audit. Condition of packaging. Condition of food. Condition of canned goods. Housekeeping.	Inform chef or manager. Discard unsatisfactory food. Review systems/training. Building maintenance to remove dampness. Store out of direct sunlight.
	Multiplication of food poisoning bacteria.	Maintain in a cool, dry condition. Food within date code. Good stock rotation.		

STEP	Hazards	Controls & critical limits	Monitoring	Corrective action*
PREPARATION	Contamination with harmful bacteria, toxic chemicals or foreign bodies.	Separation of raw and high-risk food. Use separate equipment. Colour coding. Organisation/workflow. Disposable cloths/paper roll. Minimise handling of ready-to-eat food where practical. Thoroughly wash all ready-to-eat produce and garnishes. Don't top up sauces.	Internal audit.	Inform chef or manager. Discard contaminated food. Review systems/training.
		Exclude staff with food poisoning symptoms.	Staff sickness record and exclusions.	
	Multiplication of food poisoning bacteria.	Maximum time at room temperature 30 minutes.(Critical limit 2 hours) Pre-cool salad sandwich ingredients.	Temperature of food. Time at room temperature.	Discard high-risk food left at room temperature for >2 hours.
		Minimise quantities prepared. Portion control.		Reduce quantities prepared.
THAWING	Multiplication of food poisoning bacteria.	High-risk food should be thawed in a refrigerator. Use thawed food within 24 hours. (Label)	Internal audit. Temperature of food.	Inform chef or manager. Discard food which has thawed and then been left at room temperature for >2 hours.
	Contamination with harmful bacteria, toxic chemicals or foreign bodies.	High-risk and raw food should not be thawed in the same area. Raw food should not be thawed in areas used for cooling cooked food.		Discard contaminated food. Review systems/training.
	Survival of food poisoning bacteria (during cooking).	Raw frozen food must be completely thawed, especially poultry. (Critical limit - absence of ice.)	Temperature/visual and physical checks.	Continue thawing. Allow longer thawing time in future.
COOKING/REHEATING	Survival of harmful bacteria/spores and/or toxins.	Cook thoroughly to 78°C. Critical limit 75°C (or equivalent time and temperature.) Boil liquids. Don't reheat more than once.	Core temperature of food. Internal audit. Visual checks.	Inform chef or manager. Extend cooking time until core temperature of 78°C is reached. Allow longer cooking time/higher oven temperature in future. Carry out cooking trials.
		Contingency plans. Cook/reheat just before eating.		Discard simmering high-risk liquids that have not been stirred for more than 2 hours. If less than 2 hours, stir liquid and bring to boil.
		Follow microwave procedures. Follow instruction on packaging. Stir liquids.		Call out engineer.
		Ensure frozen meat and poultry is completely thawed prior to cooking.		Implement contingency plan. Review systems/training.
	Contamination with toxic chemicals or foreign bodies.	Avoid copper and aluminium for acid food. Protect from contamination.		Repair/replace unsatisfactory equipment and pans.

STEP	Hazards	Controls & critical limits	Monitoring	Corrective action*
COOLING	Contamination with harmful bacteria, toxic chemicals or foreign bodies.	Separation of raw and high-risk food. Protect from contamination.	Internal audit. Time to cool. Temperature of food.	Inform chef or manager. Discard contaminated food. Review systems/training. Discard food if not cooled and refrigerated within critical time. Call out engineer. Repair/replace blast chiller.
	Multiplication of food poisoning bacteria, formation of toxins and/or germination of spores.	Rapid cooling (blast chiller) and refrigeration. Minimise weight/thickness of joints, e.g. 2 kgs. Cool liquids in clean, shallow trays (maximum depth 25mm.) Blast chiller (90 minutes.) 63°C to 20°C in <2 hours. (Critical limit in >3 hours.) 20°C to 7°C in <4 hours. (Critical limit in >5hours.)		
HOT HOLDING	Contamination with harmful bacteria, toxic chemicals or foreign bodies.	Protect from contamination. Sneeze guards etc. if hot holding for service. Use disinfected temperature probe.	Internal audit.	Inform chef or manager. Discard contaminated food. Review systems/training.
	Multiplication of food poisoning bacteria, formation of toxins and/or germination of spores.	Maintain at the correct temperature (minimum 63°C). (Critical limit <63°C for 2 hours.) Minimise quantities. Preheat hot holding equipment. Contingency plans.	Time and temperature of food.	Adjust thermostat. Discard any food that has been maintained at below 63°C for more than 2 hours. Call out engineer. Repair/replace equipment. Implement contingency plan.
COLD DISPLAY	Contamination with harmful bacteria, toxic chemicals or foreign bodies.	Food covered/protected, e.g. sneeze screens. Segregation of raw and high-risk food. Use disinfected temperature probe. Minimise handling, use long handled tongs/serving utensils.	Internal audit.	Inform chef or manager. Discard contaminated food. Review systems/training.
	Multiplication of food poisoning bacteria.	Food stored below 5°C. (Critical limit >8°C for 4 hours.) Good stock rotation.	Air temperature. In-between pack temperature. Temperature of food. Time above 8°C. Food is within date code.	Adjust thermostat. Discard any food >8°C for 4 hours. Call out engineer. Implement contingency plan.
SERVICE	Contamination with harmful bacteria, toxic chemicals or foreign bodies.	Protect from contamination. Minimise handling. Separate staff handling raw and high-risk food. Colour coding. Handwashing between handling soiled crockery and/or cutlery.	Internal audit. Visual inspection.	Inform chef or manager. Discard contaminated food. Review systems/training.
	Multiplication of food poisoning bacteria.	Minimise time high-risk food is at room temperature. Serve within 15 minutes of cooking, hot holding, chill storage or preparation.		

⁺ Frequency of checks and person responsible should be included. Monitoring records will usually be needed at most steps.
* Person responsible for corrective action should be included.

N.B. Effective supervision, instruction and competency training are controls at each step. High standards of personal hygiene, integrated pest management, effective cleaning and disinfection and maintenance are prerequisites to the implementation of HACCP and are not included within the HACCP control chart. However, they are controls that apply at most steps. Chemical and physical hazards are mainly dealt with through the prerequisite programmes.

Key points

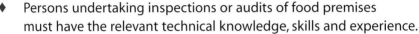

- ◆ Supervisors and managers have an essential role in producing safe food and preventing food poisoning.
- ◆ Standards ensure consistency and customer satisfaction. They are essential to facilitate control and monitoring.
- ◆ Food safety policies should demonstrate the commitment of the company to operate to high standards and produce safe food.
- ◆ Quality assurance is proactive, quality control is reactive.
- ◆ Persons undertaking inspections or audits of food premises must have the relevant technical knowledge, skills and experience.
- ◆ Training of food handlers should be carefully planned as part of a comprehensive food safety training programme.
- ◆ The effective investigation of food poisoning is essential to limit the spread of infection and provide information to assist in surveillance.
- ◆ HACCP is a food safety management system which predicts hazards and risks, enabling their removal prior to food production.

12 Food safety legislation

The law is a complex subject and most acts and regulations affecting the food industry are difficult to interpret. However, ignorance of the law is no defence in the event of a prosecution and supervisors must make a special effort to become conversant with legislation which affects their work.

This chapter includes an outline of the most important legislation relating to food and food hygiene in Scotland, England and Wales; Northern Ireland has its own legislation, although any differences are usually minor. Should information or advice be required regarding the interpretation of a particular section, or the current legislation applicable, the local environmental health officer or a solicitor should be consulted.

Legislation consists of: Acts of Parliament which are concerned with principles of legislation; regulations and orders which normally deal with specific premises or commodities in much greater detail than acts; and local acts or bylaws which are made or adopted by local authorities and are legally binding only within the area of the particular authority.

In the event of any legal query, it is always best to consult someone conversant with the specifics of both the legal system and the subject matter in question.

Acts and regulations applicable to the food industry are concerned with:

- preventing the production or sale of injurious, unsafe or unfit food;
- preventing the contamination of food and food equipment;
- the hygiene of food premises, equipment and personnel (including training);
- hygiene practices, including temperature control and the control and monitoring of hazards at points which are critical to food safety;
- the provision of sanitary accommodation, water supplies and washing facilities;
- the control of food poisoning;
- the importation of food;
- the composition and labelling of food; and
- the registration and licensing of food premises and vehicles.

The European Union

Most legislation relating to food safety is now imposed by the European Union in the form of regulations or directives. EU regulations apply without modification whereas directives require the member states to introduce their own legislation to achieve the objectives of the Directive.

Regulation (EC) No 852/2004 on the hygiene of foodstuffs
(Effective from 1st January 2006)
Article 5.

Food business operators must implement a food safety management system based on the following HACCP principles:
- **(a)** identifying hazards;
- **(b)** identifying the critical control points (CCPs) at the steps at which control is essential to prevent or eliminate a hazard or to reduce it to acceptable levels;
- **(c)** establishing critical limits at CCPs which separate acceptability from unacceptability;
- **(d)** implementing effective monitoring procedures at CCPs;
- **(e)** establishing corrective actions when a CCP is out of control;
- **(f)** establishing verification procedures
- **(g)** establishing documents and records commensurate with the nature and size of the food business. (Documents must be kept up-to-date and retained for an appropriate period.) The system must be reviewed if the product, process or any step is modified.

Article 6.

Food business operators must register with the competent authority (usually the local authority).

Significant changes in activities must be reported to the competent authority.

Article 8.

National guides to good practice shall be developed by food business sectors in consultation with competent authorities and consumer groups.

Annex II (General hygiene requirements)
Chapter I (General requirements for food premises)
- ◆ Food premises are to be kept clean and maintained in good repair and condition.
- ◆ The design, layout, construction, siting and size of food premises are to:
  - **(a)** permit adequate maintenance cleaning and/or disinfection, minimize airborne contamination, and provide adequate working space to allow for the hygienic performance of all operations;
  - **(b)** be such as to protect against the accumulation of dirt, contact with toxic materials, the shedding of particles into food and the formation of condensation or undesirable mould on surfaces;
  - **(c)** permit good food hygiene practices, including protection against contamination and, in particular, pest control; and
  - **(d)** where necessary provide suitable temperature controlled handling and storage conditions of sufficient capacity for maintaining foodstuffs at appropriate temperatures to be monitored and, where necessary, recorded.

- An adequate number of flush lavatories are to be available. Lavatories are not to open directly into rooms in which food is handled.
- An adequate number of washbasins are to be available, suitably located and designated for cleaning hands. Washbasins are to be provided with hot and cold running water, materials for cleaning, hands and for hygienic drying. Where necessary, the facilities for washing food are to be separate from the handwashing facility.
- There is to be suitable and sufficient means of natural or mechanical ventilation. Mechanical air flow from a contaminated area to a clean area is to be avoided. Ventilation systems are to be so constructed as to enable filters and other parts requiring cleaning or replacement to be readily accessible.
- Sanitary conveniences are to have adequate natural or mechanical ventilation.
- Food premises are to have adequate natural and/or artificial lighting.
- Drainage facilities are to be adequate for the purpose intended. They are to be designed and constructed to avoid the risk of contamination.
- Where necessary, adequate changing facilities for personnel are to be provided.
- Cleaning agents and disinfectants are not to be stored in areas where food is handled.

Chapter II (Specific requirements in rooms where foodstuffs are prepared, treated or processed)

(1) The design and layout of the rooms are to permit good food hygiene practices, including protection against contamination between and during operations. In particular:

   (a) floor surfaces are to be maintained in a sound condition and be easy to clean and, where necessary, to disinfect. This will require the use of impervious, washable and non-toxic materials, unless the food business operators can satisfy the competent authority that other materials used are appropriate. Where appropriate, floors are to allow adequate surface drainage;

   (b) wall surfaces are to maintained in a sound condition and be easy to clean and, where necessary to, disinfect. This will require the use of impervious, washable and non-toxic materials and require a smooth surface up to a height appropriate for the operations, unless food business operators can satisfy the competent authority that other materials used are appropriate;

   (c) ceilings and overhead fixtures are to be designed, constructed and finished so as to prevent the accumulation of dirt and to reduce condensation, the growth of undesirable moulds and the shedding of particles;

(d) windows and other openings are to be constructed to prevent the accumulation of dirt. Those which can be opened to the outside environment are, where necessary, to be fitted with insect-proof screens which can be easily removed for cleaning. Where open windows would result in contamination, windows are to remain closed and fixed during production;

(e) doors are to be easy to clean and, where necessary, to disinfect. This will require the use of smooth and non-absorbent surfaces, unless the food business operators can satisfy the competent authority that other materials used are appropriate; and

(f) surfaces (including surfaces of equipment) in areas where foods are handled and in particular those in contact with food are to be maintained in sound condition and be easy to clean and, where necessary, to disinfect. This will require the use of smooth, washable, corrosion-resistant and non-toxic materials, unless food business operators can satisfy the competent authority that other materials used are appropriate.

(2)   Adequate facilities are to be provided, where necessary, for the cleaning, disinfecting and storage of working utensils and equipment. These facilities are to be constructed of corrosion-resistant materials, be easy to clean and have an adequate supply of hot and cold water.

(3)   Adequate provision is to be made, where necessary, for washing food. Every sink or other such facility provided for the washing of food is to have an adequate supply of hot and/or cold potable water, and be kept clean, and where necessary, disinfected.

Chapter III Requirements for market stalls or mobile sales vehicles, premises used primarily as a private dwelling house, premises used occasionally for catering purposes and vending machines)

Premises and vending machines are, so far as is reasonably practicable, to be sited, designed, constructed, kept clean and maintained in good repair and condition as to avoid the risk of contamination, in particular by animals and pests.

Surfaces in contact with food are to be in a sound condition and be easy to clean and, where necessary, to disinfect.

Where necessary, there are to be facilities to maintain adequate personal hygiene and for the cleaning and, where necessary, disinfecting of working utensils and equipment.

Adequate facilities and/or arrangements for maintaining and monitoring suitable food temperature conditions are to be available.

Foodstuffs are to be placed so as to avoid the risk of contamination.

Chapter IV (Transport)

Conveyances and/or containers used for transporting foodstuffs are to be kept clean and maintained in good repair and condition to protect foodstuffs from contamination, and are, where necessary, to be designed and constructed to permit adequate cleaning and/or disinfection.

Chapter V
(Equipment requirements)

All articles, fittings and equipment with which food comes into contact are to:

(a)   be effectively cleaned and, where necessary, disinfected. Cleaning and disinfection are to take place at a frequency sufficient to avoid any risk of contamination;

(b & c) be so constructed, be of such materials and be kept in such good order, repair and condition as to minimise any risk of contamination and to enable them to be kept clean and, where necessary, to be disinfected; and

(d)   be installed in such a manner as to allow adequate cleaning of the equipment and the surrounding area. Where necessary, equipment is to be fitted with any appropriate control device to guarantee fulfilment of this Regulation's objective.

Chapter VI (Food waste)

Food waste, non-edible by-products and other refuse are to be removed from food rooms as quickly as possible, so as to avoid their accumulation.

Waste is to be deposited in closable containers (unless the competent authority agree otherwise). Containers are to be of an appropriate construction, kept in sound condition, be easy to clean and, where necessary, to disinfect.

Adequate provision is to be made for the storage of waste. Refuse stores are to be kept clean and free of animals and pests.

All waste is to be eliminated in a hygienic and environmentally friendly way and is not to constitute a direct or indirect source of contamination.

Chapter VII (Water supply)

An adequate supply of potable water must be provided and used to ensure foodstuffs are not contaminated. Ice is to be made from potable water, if it could contaminate the food. It is to be made, handled and stored to protect it from contamination.

Where heat treatment is applied to foodstuffs in hermetically sealed containers it is to be ensured that water used to cool the containers after heat treatment is not a source of contamination for the foodstuff.

Chapter VIII (Personal hygiene)

Persons working in food handling areas are to maintain a high degree of personal cleanliness and wear suitable, clean and, where necessary, protective clothing.

No person suffering from, or being a carrier of a foodborne disease, or afflicted with infected wounds, skin infections, sores or diarrhoea is to be permitted to handle food or enter any food handling area in any capacity if there is a likelihood of direct or indirect contamination. Any person so affected and employed in a food business and who is likely to come into contact with food is to report immediately the illness or symptoms, and if possible their causes, to the food business operator.

Chapter IX (Provisions applicable to foodstuffs)

Contaminated or decomposed raw materials must be rejected unless normal sorting and hygienic preparation will ensure their fitness for human consumption.

All food must be protected against contamination during handling, storage, packaging, display and distribution.

Effective pest control procedures must be implemented.

Food likely to support the reproduction of pathogenic microorganisms or the formation of toxins is not to be kept at temperatures that might result in a risk to health. Food businesses manufacturing, handling and wrapping processed foodstuffs are to have suitable rooms, large enough to separate the storage of raw materials from processed material, and sufficient separate refrigerated storage.

Where foodstuffs are to be held or served at chilled temperatures they are to be cooled as quickly as possible following the heat-processing stage, or final preparation stage if no heat process is applied, to a temperature which does not result in a risk to health.

The thawing of foodstuffs is to be undertaken in such a way as to minimise the risk of growth of pathogenic microorganisms or the formation of toxins in the foods.

Hazardous and/or inedible substances, including animal feed, are to be adequately labelled and stored in separate and secure containers.

Chapter X (Provisions applicable to the wrapping and packaging of foodstuffs)

Materials used for wrapping are not to be a source of contamination. They must be stored in such a manner that they are not exposed to a risk of contamination.

Wrapping and packaging operations are to avoid contamination of the products. The integrity and cleanliness of cans and glass jars are to be assured.

Reusable wrapping and packaging material are to be easy to clean and, where necessary, to disinfect.

Chapter XI (Heat treatment)

Heat treatment of food in hermetically sealed containers should conform to an internationally recognised standard (for example, pasteurization, ultra high temperature or sterilization). Every part of the product should achieve a given temperature for a given period of time.

Chapter XII (Training)
Food business operators are to ensure:
(1) that food handlers are supervised and instructed and/or trained in food hygiene matters commensurate with their work activity; and
(2) that those responsible for the development and maintenance of the HACCP system or for the operation of relevant guides have received adequate training in the application of the HACCP principles.

The Food Safety Act, 1990

This is the most important Act relating to the sale of food for human consumption and as such is applicable to all food premises in England, Scotland and Wales.

Section 1. 'Food' includes water which is bottled for sale or used as an ingredient (water supplied to the premises is excluded). It excludes live animals, birds or fish, animal feeding stuffs or drugs.

'Premises' includes any place, vehicle or stall.

Section 2. Extends the meaning of 'sale' to include food which is offered as a prize or reward or given away in connection with any entertainment for the public.

Section 3. Food, or ingredients, commonly used for human consumption are presumed, until the contrary is proved, to be intended for sale for human consumption.

Section 7. It is an offence to treat food so as to render it injurious to health with the intent that the food will be sold in that state. Regard shall be had to the cumulative effect of foods consumed over a long period.

Section 8. It is an offence to sell, offer for sale or have in possession for sale food intended for human consumption which fails to comply with the food safety requirements, i.e. food which has been rendered injurious to health, is unfit for human consumption or is so contaminated (whether by extraneous matter or otherwise) that it would be unreasonable to expect it to be used for human consumption in that state.

Section 9. An authorized officer of a food authority may seize or detain food (for up to 21 days) which fails to comply with food safety requirements or which is likely to cause food poisoning or a foodborne disease. Food which is seized has to be dealt with by a Justice of the Peace. Any person liable to be prosecuted in respect of such food is entitled to make representations to the Justice of the Peace. If the food is not condemned, or detained food is cleared, compensation can be claimed. Any expenses incurred in the destruction of condemned food must be paid by the owner of the food.

Section 10. An authorized officer can serve an improvement notice on the proprietor of a food business for failing to comply with regulations relating to hygiene or to the processing or treatment of food. The notice must state the grounds for non-compliance, the contraventions and measures necessary to secure compliance, and the time (not less than 14 days) allowed. Failure to comply is an offence.

Section 11. If a proprietor of a food business is convicted of an offence under the regulations and the court is satisfied that the business, any process/treatment, the construction or condition of any premises or the use or condition of any equipment involves a risk of injury to health, they shall impose a prohibition order. A prohibition order can apply to the use of a process/treatment, the premises (or part thereof) or any equipment. A copy of the prohibition order must be conspicuously fixed on the premises and contravention of the order is an offence.

The prohibition order ceases to have effect when the enforcement authority issues a certificate which states that there is no longer a health risk. The court may also impose a prohibition on the proprietor or manager participating in the management of any food business. This prohibition applies for at least six months.

Section 12. If an authorized officer of an enforcement authority is satisfied that there is an imminent risk of injury to health he may issue an emergency prohibition notice. An application for an emergency prohibition order must then be made to the court within three days of serving the notice.

The emergency prohibition notice and emergency prohibition order must be served on the proprietor and conspicuously displayed on the premises. Any contravention is an offence. An emergency prohibition notice/order ceases to have effect when the enforcement authority issues a certificate which states that there is no longer a health risk.

Section 14. It is an offence to sell, to the prejudice of the purchaser, any food which is not of the nature (different kind or variety) or substance (not containing proper ingredients) or quality (inferior, for example, stale bread) demanded by the purchaser.

Section 20. Enables proceedings to be taken against another person when the offence was due to his act or default.

Section 21. It is a defence for a person to prove that he took all reasonable precautions and exercised all due diligence to avoid the commission of the offence, by himself or by a person under his control.

In the case of persons not involved with the preparation or importation, for example, a retailer, charged with an offence under Sections 8, 14 or 15, it is a defence to prove:

    (a)   the offence was due to another person;

    (b)   that he carried out all reasonable checks or it was reasonable to rely on checks carried out by his supplier; and

    (c)   he did not know or suspect his act or omission would amount to an offence.

Sections 29 & 30. Empower an authorized officer to purchase or take samples of food, food sources, contact materials or any article or substance required as evidence.

Section 32. Empowers an authorized officer, on production of an authenticated document showing his authority, to enter any premises within his area at all reasonable hours to carry out his duties under the Act. In the case of a private dwelling-house entry cannot be demanded unless 24 hours' notice has been given to the occupier. An enforcement officer is also empowered to enter any business premises outside his area for the purpose of ascertaining whether or not there are any contraventions of the Act or regulations/orders made thereunder. Warrants may be issued by a Justice of the Peace authorizing entry, by force if necessary, if entry is refused.

Authorized officers can inspect, seize and detain records, including computer records, required as evidence. Improper disclosure of information so obtained is an offence.

Section 33. It is an offence to obstruct persons executing the provisions of the Act, including the failure to assist or provide information (unless it incriminates them) or the furnishing of false information.

Section 35. The penalty for most offences is:

♦ on conviction on indictment to an unlimited fine and/or up to two years' imprisonment;

♦ on summary conviction to a fine not exceeding the relevant amount and/or imprisonment for up to six months. (In the case of Sections 7, 8 or 14 the relevant amount is £20,000, the amount for the other sections is £5,000).

Section 40. This section empowers ministers to issue codes of practice to guide food authorities on the enforcement of food safety legislation. This is intended to assist in uniform standards of enforcement. The codes of practice are not legally binding but food authorities must have regard to them.

The Food Hygiene (England) Regulations 2005
Chill holding requirements

Food which supports the growth of pathogens or the formation of toxins must not be kept above 8°C unless:

♦ it is hot food on display;
♦ there is no health risk;
♦ it is canned or dehydrated (until opened); and
♦ it is raw food intended for cooking or further processing.

Chill holding tolerance periods

Food may be kept above 8°C if the manufacturer has undertaken a scientific assessment confirming there is no risk and the shelf-life is not exceeded.

Food on display, or for service, may be kept above 8°C for up to four hours on a single occasion. Food may also be kept above 8°C during loading or unloading or for unavoidable reasons, such as defrosting equipment or breakdowns, provided this is consistent with food safety.

Hot holding requirements

Hot food on display must not be kept below 63°C. Food may be kept below 63°C if a scientific assessment has indicated there is no health risk.

Hot food for service or display may be kept below 63°C for up to two hours on a single occasion.

Temperature Control Requirements in Scotland
Chill holding

Food should be kept in a refrigerator or a cool ventilated place or above 63°C unless:

(a)	it is undergoing preparation for sale;
(b)	it is exposed for sale or has been sold;
(c)	it is being cooled under hygienic conditions as quickly as possible to a safe temperature immediately following cooking or the final processing stage; and
(d)	being kept at ambient temperatures poses no risk to health.

Reheating of food

Food which is to be reheated before being served for immediate consumption or exposed for sale shall be raised to a temperature of not less than 82°C, unless this would result in a deterioration in its qualities.

♦ Gelatin used for bakers' confectionery filling, meat or fish products shall, immediately before use, be brought to the boil or kept at a temperature of not less than 71°C for 30 minutes.

♦ Any gelatin remaining, other than waste, shall be cooled as quickly as practicable and refrigerated or stored in a cool ventilated place.

National guides to good hygiene practice

These guides provide food businesses with practical advice on complying with food safety regulations and must be given due consideration by enforcers. They will also assist in achieving consistency of enforcement. The guides may be used in courts to illustrate good practice. However, food businesses do not have to follow the advice in any guide as they may wish to comply with the regulations in some other way.

The Food Labelling Regulations, 1996

These regulations apply in England, Scotland and Wales and require most food sold for human consumption to be labelled with:

♦ the name of the food;

♦ a list of ingredients;

♦ a 'best-before' date which provides an indication of minimum durability (shelf-life) or in the case of food which, microbiologically, is highly perishable and in consequence likely, after a short period, to constitute an immediate danger to human health, a 'use-by' date;

♦ any special storage conditions or conditions of use; and

♦ the name and address of the manufacturer, packer or seller.

The enforcement of food safety legislation in the United Kingdom

In the United Kingdom, central government has given the responsibility for protecting public health and ensuring food businesses comply with food hygiene legislation to local authorities. Officers with a wide range of qualifications, experience and expertise are employed to enable authorities to carry out the significant range of food hygiene and food safety controls that now exist. The most common local authority official involved in food hygiene control is an environmental health officer (EHO). Authorities may also appoint technical officers with specialist food qualifications. These officers are authorized to enforce the various acts and regulations.

The functions of EHOs and other authorized officers include:

♦ ensuring product safety and fitness for consumption;
♦ reducing possible sources of contamination entering the food environment;
♦ monitoring conditions and hygienic operations within the food environment;
♦ ensuring compliance with relevant legislation;
♦ establishing the integrity of management and effectiveness of control procedures; and
♦ offering professional guidance, including preventive advice, particularly when legislation is changing.

EHOs and other officers undertake the above functions:

♦ during routine visits to and inspections of food premises;
♦ whilst investigating food poisoning outbreaks and incidents;
♦ whilst investigating food complaints;
♦ by lecturing on hygiene courses and seminars and giving related talks;
♦ by using the media, for example, press releases, committee reports and hazard warnings;
♦ whilst dealing with planning and licence applications;
♦ by developing partnerships with businesses' decision-making bases in the local authority's area (often referred to as the 'Home Authority Principle'); and
♦ by developing local business forums for the exchange of information and the provision of advice.

Inspections of food premises by enforcement officers

Food hygiene inspections have two main purposes:

♦ to identify risks arising from the food businesses' activities and determine the effectiveness of the businesses' own assessment of hazards and controls; and
♦ to identify contraventions of food legislation and seek to have them corrected.

Before carrying out a food hygiene inspection, EHOs will take account of a number of issues. These will include:

♦ reviewing the premises' history – including information on operations and systems, previous complaints and responses to earlier inspection outcomes;
♦ timing of inspection – generally unannounced, although advance notice may occasionally be appropriate to ensure relevant persons are present;

◆ equipment availability, for example, calibrated temperature recording equipment;
◆ appropriate protective clothing; and
◆ assessing the need for additional expertise, for example, food examiners.

Frequency of inspections

Effective inspection programmes recognize that the frequency of inspection will vary according to the type of food business, the nature of the food, the degree of handling and the size of the business. The frequency of visits is determined by the hazards associated with the business, including the current level of compliance with food safety legislation, the confidence of the enforcement officer in management, the history of compliance and the control systems in place. Essentially, those premises posing potentially a higher risk should be inspected more frequently than those premises with a lower risk.

Businesses handling low-risk foods, with few customers, that comply with food hygiene legislation and are managed effectively may only be inspected every five years. Businesses processing high-risk food or at risk from *E coli* O157 or *Clostridium botulinum*, or supplying vulnerable consumers, are likely to be inspected at least every six months.

Action taken as a result of an inspection

During an inspection, an EHO may identify contraventions of food hygiene legislation and/or poor or unsafe food handling practices. Several options exist to remedy the contraventions and detailed guidance is found in the Food Law, Code of Practice as to the most appropriate action. The options available and potential outcomes for all food hygiene inspections include:

◆ verbal advice/warnings or informal written advice/warnings where the EHO is confident the work will be carried out. Letters should clearly differentiate between legal requirements and recommendations;
◆ an improvement notice, for contraventions of food hygiene legislation, allowing not less than 14 days to comply;
◆ the detention or seizure of unsafe food where food does not comply with the food safety requirements;
◆ an emergency prohibition notice, where there is an imminent risk of injury to health, requiring closure of the premises or prohibition of processes or use of equipment (a court will issue a prohibition order if the proprietor is convicted and there is a risk of injury to health);
◆ a formal caution where an offence exists but it is not considered in the public interest to prosecute through the courts; and
◆ prosecution, where it is considered in the public interest.

The defence of 'due diligence', in the Food Safety Act 1990 is of specific note. The

Act creates a number of offences known as 'strict liability'. It does not matter that the accused did not intend to break the law. The mere fact that there is clear evidence that the statute has been contravened is sufficient for a conviction. This regime of strict liability was perceived as causing injustice if a person was held to have committed an offence for which he had no responsibility, or because of an accident or some cause completely beyond his control. To create a balance of fairness, the defence of 'due diligence' was included.

The Act specifically states that it is a defence to prove that all reasonable precautions were taken and all due diligence exercised to avoid the offence. Through legal precedent, various principles have been confirmed as necessary if a defence is to succeed. Some positive steps will always be required. Taking reasonable precautions involves the setting up of a system of control having regard to the nature of the risks involved. Due diligence involves securing the proper operation of that system. Where there is a reasonable precaution then it should be taken. Written records are not a legal requirement; however, satisfactory records may be useful to assist a due diligence defence.

The Food Standards Agency

The Food Standards Agency was established on 1st April 2000. Its role is 'to protect public health from risks which may arise in connection with the consumption of food and otherwise to protect the interest of consumers in relation to food'.

The core values of the Agency are to:
- put the consumer first;
- be open and accessible; and
- be an independent voice.

The Agency's functions are to:
- provide advice and information to the public and to the government on food safety from farm to fork, nutrition and diet;
- protect consumers through effective enforcement and monitoring; and
- support consumer choice through promoting accurate and meaningful labelling.

The Food Standards Agency is led by a board and accounts to Parliament through Health Ministers. The headquarters are based in London. Scottish, Welsh and Northern Irish Executives of the Agency are responsible for implementing policies on food issues specific to each country within the Agency's framework.

The Agency has responsibility for:
- food safety, contaminants, nutrition, additives and labelling;
- animal feed and veterinary public health;
- the performance of Local Authority enforcement;
- the Meat Hygiene Service; and
- research.

Website: www.foodstandards.gov.uk

Appendix 1 Characteristics of important UK pathogens

Pathogen Infective dose	Source	Food vehicle	Growth temperature range (°C) optimum	Growth pH range optimum	Onset period duration	Typical symptoms Oxygen reqs.	*Additional specific controls
Bacillary dysentery *Shigella sonnei* *Shigella flexneri* Very low	Infected person/carriers - sewage/manure, water	Contaminated foods, water, milk, salads, parsley, fruits, sandwich fillings, bakery products, e.g. cream, filled pastries and shellfish. (Faecal/oral route)	N/A	N/A	1 - 7 days usually 4 days 2 - 16 days	F, A, N, V, D (may contain blood/mucus) N/A	• Exclusion of ill food handlers, or if close contact of case • Ensure safe water supplies • Satisfactory disposal of sewage • Heat treatment of milk • Approved suppliers • Washing/blanching of fruits and salads
Campylobacter jejuni Low	Soil, sewage, poultry, water, animals, raw meat and raw milk. Cats, dogs, rodents and some wild birds (ducks, geese and seagulls)	Raw milk, handling raw or eating undercooked chicken, other meats, meat products, water, bottled milk pecked by birds	28 to 46 37 to 43	4.9 to 9.5 7	1 to 11 days usually 2 to 5 days 1 to 7 days	Headache, F, D (often bloodstained) A (colicky), N V (rare) A, D, V (rare) Obligate microaerophilic	• Reduce contamination levels of raw meat/poultry (slaughterhouse hygiene) • Hygiene of harvesters • Washing hands after handling raw poultry/meat • Keep animals/pets out of food rooms/businesses • Avoid cross-contamination • Chlorination of water (care with irrigation) • Heat treatment of milk • Thorough cooking
Escherichia coli O157 Very low (fatalities especially young and elderly)	Intestinal tracts of humans and animals, sewage, animal carcases and water	Raw or rare meats and poultry, raw milk and milk products, unprocessed cheese, salads, fruit, undercooked burgers/mince, cooked meats, buffets, fruit juice and seafoods	3 to 46 37	4.4 to 9.5 7	1 to 6 days 2 weeks or longer	D (watery/bloody) A, N Up to 30% develop haemolytic uraemic syndrome Facultative anaerobe	• Reduce contamination levels of raw meat especially at slaughterhouses • Effective separation of raw meat and ready-to-eat food (avoid cross-contamination) • Thorough cooking of meat especially burgers and mince • Double-washing salad vegetables and ready-to-eat fruit • Heat treatment of milk/apple juice • Hygiene of harvesters
Listeria monocytogenes Probably low for immuno-compromised	Soil, sewage/effluent, water, vegetation and other environmental sources, carriers, birds and mammals	Raw milk, soft cheese, coleslaw, ice-cream, raw vegetables, raw and cooked meat, raw and under-cooked poultry, raw and smoked fish, pâté, jellied pork tongue, fermented sausages, salads and cook-chill products	−1.5 to 42 30 to 37	4.4 to 9.5 7	1 to 70 days 48 to 72 hrs	Flu-like symptoms N, V, M, F, D, septicaemia, meningitis and abortion in pregnant women Anaerobic (microaerophilic)	• Strict stock rotation of refrigerated food and use within date code • Pregnant women to avoid high-risk foods, especially soft cheese and pâté • Thorough reheating of cook-chill foods • Avoid cross-contamination, especially in factories • Washing of ready-to-eat salads etc. • Safe sewage disposal/care with irrigation • Use of clean vehicles/crates for transport of raw vegetables
Typhoid (Salmonella Typhi) ** *Paratyphoid -* *salmonella paratyphi* Low (some fatalities)	Carriers, sewage/manure, water	Water, milk, cooked meat, dairy products, coconut, salad dressings, salads, some fruit and vegetables (manure). (Faecal/oral route)	N/A	N/A	1 - 3 weeks (Paratyphoid usually shorter) 1 to 8 weeks	F, N, M, headache. Rose spots on trunk. Slow pulse. Anorexia. Spleen enlargement. Constipation or sometimes D (severe) N/A	• Exclusion of ill food handlers • Ensure safe water supplies • Satisfactory disposal of sewage • Heat treatment of milk • Approved suppliers • Exclude carriers • Washing/blanching of fruits and salads • Hygiene for harvesters

Key: V=vomiting A=abdominal pain D=diarrhoea F=fever N=nausea M=malaise * Controls in addition to effective prerequisite programmes and HACCP
** Paratyphoid is less severe and symptoms may be similar to salmonella food poisoning.

Appendix 1 Characteristics of important UK pathogens

Pathogen Infective dose	Source	Growth temperature range (°C) optimum	Growth pH range optimum	Onset period duration	Typical symptoms Oxygen reqs.	*Additional specific controls
Bacillus cereus Toxin in food (Tf) Toxin in intestine (Ti) Medium	Soil, vegetation, dust and a variety of cereals, especially rice, dried foods and spices. Intestinal tract of humans.	5 to 48 28 to 35	4.4 to 9.3 7	(Tf) 1to 5 hrs 12 to 24 hrs (Ti) 8 to 16 hrs 1 to 2 days	V, A, N, D (some) A, D (watery), V (some) F Facultative anaerobe Spore former	• Thorough cooking, hot-hold (>63°C) or rapid cooling • Storing at correct temperatures • Avoid rewarming • Avoid cross-contamination
Clostridium botulinum Toxin in food (Tf) Very low (fatalities common)	Soil, vegetables, intestinal tracts of fish and mammals	3 to 50 20 to 30 (type E)	4.6 to 9.0 7	2 to 8 days usually several months	Difficulties in swallowing, talking and breathing, vertigo, double-vision and paralysis of cranial nerves Anaerobic Spore former	• Strict control over processing, low-acid canned foods (pH >4.5) • Use of nitrates • Discard blown cans or those with holes or defective seams • Thorough cooking • Strict control over smoking and handling of smoked fish (store in freezer) • Care in gutting and preparing raw fish • Strict attention to the shelf-life of vacuum packed food (refrigerate) • Avoid cross-contamination • Temperature control
Clostridium perfringens Toxin in intestine (Ti) Usually high	Soil, sediment (widespread), intestinal tracts of humans and animals/sewage, raw meat, dust and insects	10 to 52 43 to 47	5.0 to 8.9 7	8 to 22 hrs usually 12 to 18 hrs 12 to 48 hrs	A, D, V (rare) Anaerobic Spore former	• Eat immediately after cooking, store above 63°C or rapid cooling and refrigeration within 1.5 hours of reaching 63°C. Strict temp control. • Joints should not exceed a size of 2.25kg • Thorough reheating of foods • Separate raw/high-risk foods • Double-wash vegetables
Salmonella spp. Infection Medium (low in milk and high fat foods such as chocolate)	Water, sewage, soil, birds, insects, carriers, intestinal tracts of animals, especially poultry and swine, raw meat, eggs, milk, melons, terrapins, rodents and reptiles	7 to 47 37	3.8 to 9.0 7	6 to 72 hrs usually 12 to 36 hrs Upto 10 days in low dose outbreaks 1 to 7 days	A, D, V, F, N, headache Facultative anaerobe	• Sterilization and strict control of animal foodstuff • Slaughterhouse hygiene • Safe sewage disposal and chlorination of water • Screening of carriers or suspects • Avoid products made with raw eggs and not fully cooked. Use pasteurized egg. • Separation of raw/high-risk food • Thorough thawing and cooking of frozen poultry • Avoid raw milk, use heat treated • Temperature control • Vaccination of poultry • Acidification and reduction of aw
Staphylococcus aureus Toxin in food (Ti) Medium	Hands, throats and noses of humans, boils and cuts, raw milk from cows or goats with mastitis and skin and hides of animals	7 to 48 10 to 45 (for toxin production) 37	3.8 to 10.0 7	1 to 7 hrs 6 to 24 hrs	A, V (mainly), D (some), N collapse and subnormal temperatures Facultative anaerobe	• Avoid handling food, use utensils • Good personal hygiene, especially regarding handwashing • Exclude handlers with respiratory infections involving coughing or sneezing • Cover cuts with waterproof dressings • Exclude persons with boils or septic cuts • Avoid the use of raw milk • Refrigeration of high-risk food • Rapid cooling, precool salad ingredients

Key: V=vomiting A=abdominal pain D=diarrhoea F=fever N=nausea M=malaise * Controls in addition to effective prerequisite programmes and HACCP

Glossary

Acute disease	A disease which develops rapidly and produces symptoms quickly after infection. Patients soon recover, or die.
Additive	A chemical added to food, e.g. a preservative, a colouring or flavouring agent.
Aerobic	Using oxygen.
Aerobic colony count	The count of viable aerobic bacteria per gram of product (based on the number of colonies grown on nutrient agar plate).
Algae	Simple plants capable of photosynthesis and most commonly found in aquatic environments or damp soil, for example, seaweed and spirogyra (forms bright green slimy masses in ponds).
Allergen	Any substance, usually a protein, which is capable of inducing an allergy.
Allergy	An identifiable immunological response to food or food additives, which may involve the respiratory system, the gastrointestinal tract, the skin or the central nervous system. In severe cases this may result in anaphylactic shock.
Ambient temperature	The temperature of the surroundings. Usually refers to the room temperature.
Anaerobic	Using little or no oxygen.
Antibiotic	A drug used to destroy pathogenic bacteria within human or animal bodies.
Antiseptic	A substance that prevents the growth of bacteria and moulds, specifically on or in the human body.
Aseptic	Free from microorganisms.
A_W (water activity)	A measure of the water available to microorganisms in food.

Bactericide	A substance which destroys bacteria.
Binary fission	Asexual method of reproduction by the division of the nucleus into two daughter nuclei, followed by similar division of the cell body. The method of reproduction used by bacteria.
Biodegradable	Chemicals and materials which can be broken down by bacteria or other biological means (usually during sewage treatment).

Carrier	A person who harbours, and may transmit, pathogenic organisms without showing signs of illness.
Chronic disease	A disease which usually develops slowly and symptoms last for a prolonged period.
Chronic poison	A substance which is used at low concentration and relies on repeated intake by the target pest to ensure elimination.
Cleaning	The process of removing soil, food residues, dirt, grease and other objectionable matter.
Clean surface	A surface which is free from residual film or soil, has no objectionable odour, is not greasy to touch and will not discolour a white paper tissue wiped over it.
Competent authority	The central authority of a member state competent to ensure compliance with relevant regulations, or any other authority to which that central authority has delegated that competence.
Contamination	The presence or introduction of a hazard. (EC Regulation No. 852/2004)
Controlled atmosphere packing	The packaging of food in an atmosphere that is different from the normal composition of air, the gases being precisely adjusted to specific concentration which are maintained throughout storage.
Critical control point (CCP)	A step in the process at which control can be applied and is essential to prevent or eliminate a food safety hazard or reduce it to an acceptable level.
Cross-contamination	The transfer of bacteria from contaminated food (usually raw) to ready-to-eat foods by direct contact, drip or indirect contact using a vehicle such as the hands or a cloth.

Danger zone of bacterial growth	The temperature range within which the multiplication of most pathogenic bacteria is possible, i.e. from 5°C to 63°C. Most rapid growth takes place between 20°C and 50°C.
Dehydrate	To remove water.
Detergent	A chemical that facilitates the removal of grease and food particles and promotes cleanliness.
Disinfectant	A chemical used for disinfection.
Disinfection	The reduction of microorganisms to a level that will not lead to harmful contamination nor spoilage of food. The term disinfection normally refers to the treatment of premises, surfaces and equipment, but may also be applied to the treatment of skin.
Epidemiology	The study of disease of people and animals, including incidence, sources, causes, mode of spread, distribution and controls.
First-aid materials	Suitable and sufficient bandages and dressings, including water-proof dressings and antiseptic.
Foodborne disease	An illness resulting from the consumption of food (or water) contaminated by pathogenic microorganisms (and/or toxins) which do not need to multiply within the food to cause illness.
Food business	Means any undertaking, whether for profit or not, and whether public or private, carrying out any of the activities related to any stage of production, processing and distribution of food.
Food handling	Any operation in the production, preparation, processing, packaging, storage, transport, distribution and sale of food.
Food hygiene	The measures and conditions necessary to control hazards and to ensure fitness for human consumption of a foodstuff taking into account its intended use. (EC Regulation No. 852/2004)
Food poisoning	An acute illness of sudden onset caused by the recent consumption of contaminated or poisonous food.
Fungi	Plants unable to synthesize their own food and usually parasitic or saprophytic. Include single-celled microscopic yeasts, moulds, mildews and toadstools.
Fungicide	A substance that kills fungi and mould.
Galvanized metal	Iron or steel which has been coated with zinc for protection against corrosion.
Gastroenteritis	An inflammation of the stomach and intestinal tract that normally results in diarrhoea.
Grease trap	A device fitted into a drainage system to prevent fat and grease entering the sewer.
Hazard	A biological, chemical or physical agent in, or condition of, food with the potential to cause harm (an adverse health effect) to the consumer. (NB most biological hazards are microbiological.)
High-risk foods	Ready-to-eat foods which, under favourable conditions, support the multiplication of pathogenic bacteria and are intended for consumption without treatment which would destroy such organisms.
Immunity	The ability to resist an invading organism so that the body does not develop the disease.
Incubation period	The period between infection (or ingestion) and the first signs of illness.
Infective dose	The number of a particular microorganism required under normal circumstances to produce clinical signs of a disease.

Moulds	Microscopic plants (fungi) that may appear as woolly patches on food.
Mycotoxin	A toxin produced by some moulds.
Neurotoxin	A toxin that affects the nervous system.
Onset period	The period between consumption of the food and the first signs of illness (where incubation of microorganisms within the body does not take place).
Optimum	Best.
Pasteurisation	A heat process used to reduce the number of microorganisms to a safe level. Pasteurised food must be stored under refrigeration.
Pathogen	Disease-producing organism.
Pest	Any living creature capable of directly or indirectly contaminating food.
Pesticide	A chemical used to kill pests.
pH	An index used as a measure of acidity or alkalinity.
Potable water	Water meeting the minimum requirements laid down in Council Directive 98/83/EC of 3 November 1998 on the quality of water intended for human consumption.
Primary production	Those stages in the food chain up to and including, for example, harvesting, slaughtering, milking and fishing.
Protozoa	Single-celled organisms which form the basis of the food chain. Some are pathogenic, e.g. cryptosporidium.
Quats	A popular name for quaternary ammonium compounds.
Residual insecticide	A long-lasting insecticide applied in such a way that it remains active for a considerable period of time.
Risk	The likelihood of a hazard occurring in food.
Risk assessment	The process of identifying hazards, assessing risks and evaluating their significance.
Safe food	Food which is free of contaminants and will not cause illness, harm or injury.
Sanitizer	A chemical agent used for cleansing and disinfecting surfaces and equipment.
Spore	A resistant resting-phase of bacteria which protects them against adverse conditions.
Sterile	Free from all living organisms.
Sterilization	A process that destroys all living organisms.
Total viable count	The total number of living cells detectable in a sample. The number of cells is assessed from the number of colonies which develop on incubation of a suitable medium which has been inoculated with the sample of bacteria.
Toxins	Poisons produced by pathogens.
Viruses	Microscopic pathogens that multiply in living cells of their host.
Yeast	A single-celled fungus which reproduces by budding and grows rapidly on certain foodstuffs, especially those containing sugar. Yeasts are the chief agents of fermentation. (Sugar converted to alcohol and carbon dioxide.)
Zoonoses	Diseases which can pass from animal to man and vice versa.

Index